Social Work
&
Mental Disorder

A Practical Guide for Social Workers
by David Beech

D1585963

Second Edition

Copyright © David Beech 1991

ISBN 0 948680 24 5

The Author

David Beech was Senior Lecturer in Social Care at Stafford College of Further Education.

After training and experience in general and psychiatric nursing, he became a Mental Welfare Officer and later a Senior MWO with Wolverhampton Health Department. Following the establishment of Social Services Departments in 1971, he trained as a Psychiatric Social Worker in Manchester. Later, he became an Assistant Area Officer in Wolverhampton.

He is a past Secretary and Chairman of Wolverhampton Association for Mental Health and Secretary of the Staffordshire Association for Mental Welfare. His first book, "Mental Illness and the Social Worker" was published in 1982, and a much extended and updated version, "Social Work and Mental Disorder" in 1986. This new edition is a testimony to the popularity of his previous books.

During the past eight years, he has played an important part in the training of Approved Social Workers in the Midlands and Potteries. He is now a freelance trainer.

Author's Note

In order to avoid the use of a multiplicity of gender pronouns, certain conventions have been adopted throughout this book.

While male includes female and vice versa, the Approved Social Worker (ASW) has been assumed to be female, the patient male and the nearest relative either sex.

David Beech   October 1991

Contents Guide

1. Introduction   5
   The Mental Health Act 1983

2. Definitions of Mental Disorder   6

3. Models of Mental Illness   8
   The Non-Medical Model; The Medical Model

4. Neuroses   11
   Anxiety States; Phobia; Obsessive-Compulsive
   Neurosis; Reactive Depression

5. Psychoses   17
   Organic Psychosis; Acute & Chronic;
   Senile Dementia; Multi-Infarct Brain Failure;
   Affective Disorders; Manic-Depressive Psychosis;
   Endogenous Depression; Mania & Hypomania

6. Schizophrenia   28
   Simple Schizophrenia; Hebephrenic Schizophrenia
   Catatonic Schizophrenia; Paranoid Schizophrenia
   Paraphrenia

7. Social Work with Schizophrenics   35

8. Mental Handicap or Mental Impairment?   38

9. Psychopathic Disorder   41

10. The Approved Social Worker   44
   Functions & Powers; Some Elements of the Social
   Work Task; The Referral; The Interview; Obligation
   to Patients' Relatives; The Removal; Negotiations
   with Doctors; The Role of the ASW in Admissions

11. The Nearest Relative   60
   Identification; Rights & Powers

12. Admission to Hospital or Guardianship   65

Informal Admission; Compulsory Admission
Applications & Medical Recommendations;
Admission for Assessment; Emergency Admission
for Assessment; Admission for Treatment;
Admission & Renewal Criteria; Appeals for Discharge;
Guardianship Orders; Entry under Part X

13. Admission through the Courts   81

Remand to Hospital for Reports; Remand to Hospital
for Treatment; Interim Hospital Order; Hospital &
Guardianship Order; Restriction Order & Direction;
Transfer Direction; Criminal Procedure (Insanity) Acts

14. Consent to Treatment   87

Consent and Second Opinion; Consent or Second Opinion

15. Mental Health Review Tribunals   91

Part II Patients; Part III Patients; How to Apply
& Procedure; The Hearing; The Social Work Role;
Tribunal Powers

16. Some Functions of the Local Authority   98

17. The Mental Health Act Commission   100

18. Children & Young People   101

Consent to Treatment; Secure Accommodation

19. Medication   103

Neurosis, Anxiety, etc.; Depression; Mania;
Schizophrenia; Senile Dementia

Step-by-Step through the Mental Health Act   109

Suggestions for Further Reading   110

Subject Index   111

Introduction

The Mental Health Act 1983

The Mental Health Act 1983 has effected significant changes in the law relating to mentally disordered persons. In particular, it has changed some of the definitions of mental disorder, especially in the area of those with learning disabilities (mental handicap). It represents a shift of emphasis away from the clinical freedom of the psychiatrist towards a more legalistic approach which seeks to offer greater protection to patients. It has strengthened the social worker's role in respect of admissions, reduced the powers of guardianship, increased patients' opportunities to be heard by Mental Health Review Tribunals, put limits on treatment without consent and introduced the Mental Health Act Commission to monitor the working of the Act.

Often, these changes represent a compromise between the conflicting evidence of interest and pressure groups. This is in contrast to the background of general agreement and desire for change which led to the 1959 Act. Thus the 1983 Act contains inherent areas of potential tension and disagreement.

The Act requires the Approved Social Worker (ASW) to possess *"appropriate competence in dealing with persons who are suffering from mental disorder"* (Section 114(2)). Thus the Approved Social Worker must know the law, as it affects her role and duties, sufficiently well to ensure compliance with it. She must also have enough knowledge of mental disorder to be able to recognise it, to be aware of its consequences for the client and his family, to communicate effectively with other professionals and to mobilise appropriate resources to deal with it.

On its own, no single book will enable the Approved Social Worker to do all of this well. Hopefully this one will make some contribution to that task.

5

Two

Definitions of Mental Disorder

Definitions and terminology are contained in Part 1 of the Mental Health Act 1983, and there are several changes from those of the 1959 Act.

First, a wide ranging general definition is given in Section 1(2) which is sufficient for Admissions for Assessment under Sections 2 and 4 and for the use of Sections 135 and 136.

"Mental disorder" means "mental illness, arrested or incomplete development of mind, psychopathic disorder and any other disorder or disability of mind..."

"Mental illness" remains undefined and should be construed as an ordinary person would use the term. In effect, it is a matter for professional judgment.

"Mental handicap" (learning disabilities) is included in this broad definition. Thus people with learning disabilities can, if appropriate, be admitted to hospital for assessment but not for treatment nor to guardianship unless "impairment" is present.

Certain forms of behaviour are explicitly excluded from being regarded as mental disorder when they occur alone in an otherwise "normal" person. These are promiscuity or other immoral conduct, sexual deviancy or dependence on alcohol or drugs.

The Act then identifies three other specific forms of mental disorder:

Severe mental impairment is "a state of arrested or incomplete development of mind which includes severe impairment of intelligence and social functioning and is associated with abnormally aggressive or seriously irresponsible conduct..."

6

Mental impairment is "a state of arrested or incomplete development of mind (not amounting to severe mental impairment) which includes *significant* impairment of intelligence and social functioning and is associated with abnormally aggressive or seriously irresponsible conduct..."

Psychopathic disorder is " a persistent disorder or disability of mind (whether or not including significant impairment of intelligence) which *results* in abnormally aggressive or seriously irresponsible conduct..."

In order for a patient to be admitted to hospital for treatment or to guardianship, one or more forms of specific mental disorder must be present. Thus people with learning disabilities must also display the additional behavioural disorder of "impairment" before being subjected to these powers.

Note: While the 1959 Act contained age limits beyond which a person could not be admitted or detained in hospital compulsorily as suffering from psychopathic disorder or mental subnormality, these have been removed in the 1983 Act. Similarly, the definition of the 1959 Act that psychopathic disorder should be susceptible to medical treatment as a condition of admission has been removed. However, it returns as an *additional* criterion for admissions under Section 3.

Three

Models of Mental Illness

There are several schools of thought about mental illness, but two main views can be identified. These I shall call the "medical" and the "non-medical" models.

The Non-Medical Model

This represents the minority view of mental illness; indeed the very term "illness" is rejected. The hypothesis of "illness" and the evidence on which it is based is regarded as only one of the many possible hypotheses which might explain why such people are behaving in unusual, strange or bizarre ways. It has not been proved, so it is stated, that it is an "illness" which is the reason for such behaviour and therefore, as an unproven hypothesis, it is inherently invalid.

Such a view leads to conflict with the medical establishment especially about schizophrenia, which has tended to become a major battlefield. The medical view regards it as an illness, the non-medical view as perhaps the product of faulty relationships. In the absence of proof, it is impossible to be certain but easy to be dogmatic.

R D Laing suggests that schizophrenia is an individual's response to his adverse environment, a role which he adopts in order to survive. *"Without exception, the experience and behaviour that gets labelled schizophrenia is a special strategy that a person invents in order to live in an unliveable situation."* (Laing 1970)

To the Laingian, the root cause of schizophrenia is faulty, traumatic family relationships which scapegoat one member. In order to survive in such a family, the scapegoat has to modify his behaviour. This modification, though necessary to him, appears "abnormal" to others and is eventually labelled as schizophrenia.

8

T S Szasz rejects the view that mental illness is analogous to physical illness. He does so on the grounds that mental illness has no definite signs and symptoms. This means that it is diagnosed in terms of communication between the doctor and the patient and on the doctor's concept of a normal, healthy state. However, both communication and normality are subjective and will be coloured by the doctor's cultural background, his prejudices and differences between him and the patient. It cannot therefore be scientific or objective.

Szasz goes on to attack what he calls "institutional psychiatry" which has a vested, often pecuniary, interest in the diagnosis (or manufacture) and treatment of "mental illness". He equates diagnostic procedures and medical treatment of mental illness with the witchfinders and with the Spanish Inquisition. "Mental illness", unless due to organic lesions of the brain itself, only exists when it is diagnosed by a doctor. (Szasz 1961)

If the non-medical model is correct, and at present it is neither proved nor disproved, then medical treatment for mental illness must be ineffective. If this is so, then social work intervention in an individual or family may be appropriate or even curative. However, supporters of the medical model attack their opponents for clouding an already misty picture and for excluding clients from the benefits of existing methods of treatment.

The Medical Model

This seeks to equate mental illness with physical illness and is the most widely held view at present. It talks of definite signs and symptoms and looks for causes in the physiology and biochemistry of the body.

Acceptance of this model entails the acceptance of treatment by medical methods, in a medical setting, under medical direction. In this model, the contribution of social work is peripheral. It is a source of information, of liaison with people and organisations outside the hospital or a means of admitting and retaining the patient to and for treatment. Within such a model, the hospital and its medical staff are of prime importance. Teamwork may exist but the captain is readily identifiable. The credibility, influence and status of other team members depend upon how closely they accept the doctor's authority, expertise and leadership and upon how useful they prove themselves to be to him.

If it is essential for workers to accept the medical model, then it is just as essential for the client to play the appropriate role. He must become a "patient", accept medical treatment, adopt a sick role and, hopefully, recover.

In spite of its uncertainties, imperfections and problems, the medical model is predominant. Because of this, it holds the key to such treatment resources as do exist. In most places it is the model with which social workers and their clients must come to terms as well as they can. Generally, the alternative is to exclude the client from such help as is available. Because of the centrality of the medical model in current practice, this model will become the backcloth for this book.

Mental illness is one of the major health problems of our time. Statistically, it will affect approximately one person in seven at some time. It is slightly more common in women than in men and its incidence increases sharply in both sexes over the age of 65. Fortunately only a minority of affected people will require treatment in hospital, but nevertheless almost half the total number of National Health Service hospital beds are occupied by mentally disordered patients (this includes the mentally handicapped). There are two broad categories of mental illness, viz. *neurosis* and *psychosis*, occurring in the proportion of 19:1. The next step is to look at each of them in some detail.

Four

Neuroses

1. Neurotic behaviour can be described as a maladaptive, inadequate or insufficient method of coping with a stress. Using this definition, we all behave neurotically at some time.

2. A neurotic reaction may result from a major stressful episode or from an accumulation of relatively minor stresses. The susceptibility of an individual to such a reaction may vary according to his circumstances at the time. It may be precipitated by a social or emotional event or by a physical illness or it may be superimposed on another mental illness.

3. Such behaviour may have its source in our early childhood (the psycho-analytical view) or it may be the result of learning and conditioning.

4. Neurotic behaviour only becomes an "illness" when it interferes with the individual's ability to lead a "normal" (i.e. socially acceptable) life. The quality of the individual's reaction will tend to be in accordance with his underlying personality.

5. Though it may be exaggerated, neurotic behaviour is qualitatively normal. It tends to affect only one aspect of personality

6. The neurotic has insight into his condition.

7. In general, a neurotic will accept and co-operate with treatment, provided it gives him greater benefit than does his neurosis.

In the treatment of neurosis, the medical model is less well entrenched. Purely medical treatment consists of the "minor tranquillisers", such as Valium or Librium, which tend to reduce the associated tension and anxiety rather than solve the underlying problem. However, used as a short-term measure, they may open the way to other forms of intervention. Long-term use may produce additional problems associated with dependence on the drugs and lead to problems when they are withdrawn.

This means that there is room for social workers, clinical psychologists and analysts as well as doctors in offering treatment. There is rarely a simple effective cure.

Individual or group psychotherapy, analysis, behaviour modification techniques, self-help groups, etc., may all be used and may be successful. It may be possible to modify the degree of stress in the individual's environment.

Admission to hospital may be appropriate if the condition is acute but, if subsequent discharge is to an unchanged, stressful environment, in-patient treatment may have little long-term value. It may be more appropriate for treatment to take place on a domiciliary, outpatient or day care basis.

Some Common Examples of Neuroses

1. Anxiety States

A sufficiently high level of fear in any individual will result in a chain of emotional and physiological responses. However, in predisposed individuals a lower level of stressful stimuli may give rise to the same responses to a lesser degree. This may result in a state of generalised anxiety and tension which is "free floating" rather than attached to a specific focus. It may be accompanied by somatic symptoms and and these may be sufficiently severe to interfere with the quality of life.

2. Phobia

This may be described as a specific anxiety state, focused on a common object or situation, which may provoke a reaction of panic in an individual quite out of keeping with its effect on others. An obsessional component is often present.

As a result of the overwhelming fear, the individual may be unable to think or act rationally; thought-blocking may occur and he may experience depersonalisation (an automaton-like feeling of unreality) and derealisation (the environment taking on a dream-like or nightmarish quality).

There are a number of theories as to the cause of phobias, e.g.

(a) *Constitutional*

This suggests a genetic predisposition to react maladaptively to stress. This theory is supported by some studies of identical twins who have been reared apart.

(b) *Psycho-analytical*

This suggests a failure to resolve earlier conflict, e.g. at the oedipal stage of development. This leads to fixation and subsequent neurosis. Such conflicts may be repressed at latency only to re-emerge at adolescence.

(c) *Behaviourist*

This suggests that a neurosis is a learned pattern of maladaptive behaviour in response to stress in the individual's environment.

Treatment

(a) Physical - the use of tranquillisers. These relieve anxiety but have little effect on its cause.

(b) Psychotherapy - either with an individual alone or in a group.

(c) Psycho-analysis - which tends to be prolonged and expensive, and thus is little used in the NHS.

(d) Behaviour modification - using techniques based on learning theory, reciprocal inhibition, etc. These techniques are becoming more widely used with promising results.

13

3. Obsessive-Compulsive Neurosis

This is characterised by a recurring thought or pattern of behaviour with a compulsive quality which the patient feels the need to resist but fails. The patient is often aware that it is irrational but resistance leads to tension and anxiety.

Such thoughts are often associated with fears of dirt, disease or contamination. The behaviour may have a ritualistic quality, e.g. touching things "to prevent harm". There is often an undercurrent of guilt and self-doubt.

It can so interfere with normal life as to become crippling and may be accompanied by anxiety and depression.

It is more common in the "anankastic" personality, i.e. introverted, meticulous, rigid people with high standards who become upset if their routine is disturbed. It is often associated with hypochondriasis.

It affects both sexes and all social classes and tends to occur in adolescence or early adulthood. It tends to be chronic, to run a fluctuating course with remissions and recurrences. Onset may be provoked by stress, a depressing event or illness.

Treatment may be disappointing. Minor tranquillisers or anti-depress-ants may help, accompanied by supportive psychotherapy. In severe and/or intractable cases, Electro-Convulsive Therapy (ECT) may cause the symptoms to recede at least temporarily. As a last resort, psycho-surgery may be considered.

4. Reactive Depression

Sometimes called "neurotic" or "exogenous" depression, this is held by some doctors to be at one end of a depressive continuum, with "endogenous" depression (q.v.) at the other. There is always a component of "loss" present in this form of depression. It may follow a bereavement, an illness (especially one involving amputation), redundancy, theft, retirement, bankruptcy, etc.

14

Symptoms

1. A situation of loss of an object, person, health, etc., significant to the individual.

2. A mood of sadness and preoccupation about the loss.

3. A diurnal variation of mood may be present. Typically the depression may be less marked on waking and become more marked as the day goes on.

4. There is often an improvement of mood in supportive company.

5. Sleep may be disturbed especially with initial insomnia (being unable to get off to sleep) and/or fitful sleep.

6. Waking may be late as a consequence.

7. Appetite may be reduced, but some individuals may derive comfort from eating.

8. Weight gain or loss will vary according to appetite.

9. Suicide risk may be present, especially 3-6 months after the precipitating loss. The risk may often decrease if the individual can derive help and support, e.g. from doctor, nurse, social worker, Samaritans, etc.

10. Physical symptoms, e.g. loss of appetite, weight-loss, constipation, retardation, may occur if the time-scale extends without improvement.

11. Delusions of guilt, lack of worth, etc. may appear later as the time-scale extends.

Treatment

a. Physical - anti-depressant drugs (see later after "endogenous depression").

b. ECT - usually considered later, when drugs do not produce an improvement, as its use may increase anxiety.

No medical treatment will restore the lost person or object. Considerable social work involvement is likely to be needed to help the client adjust to his or her loss, to come to terms with it and its effects and to make whatever changes to his or her lifestyle which may be appropriate. Readers are referred to another title in the PEPAR Publications series, "Coping with Loss" (Second Edition), by Roy V Lascelles.

Five

Psychoses

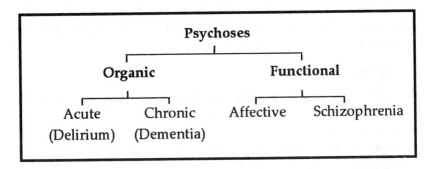

1. A psychosis is a severe mental illness.

2. Little is proven about the aetiology of functional psychoses but theories abound.

3. Psychotic behaviour is qualitatively abnormal.

4. All aspects of the individual's personality are affected.

5. The individual does not have insight into his condition.

6. Compulsory admission to hospital for treatment may be necessary.

7. At present, most treatment is aimed at target symptoms because the underlying disease process (if any) is not understood. Because of this, complete cure is uncertain.

The psychoses may be classified as "organic", i.e. of known aetiology, or as "functional", i.e. of unknown (or unproven) aetiology.

The stress of the onset of a psychotic illness may precipitate a marked neurotic reaction which may be more obvious in the early stages than the underlying psychosis.

17

Organic Psychoses

These are caused by a known and demonstrable disorder of the brain. They therefore fit most closely into the "illness" concept of the medical model. They may be acute (delirium) or chronic (dementia). The cause may be located in the brain (intrinsic), or elsewhere in the body (extrinsic).

A. Acute

The aged and young children are especially susceptible to acute organic psychoses (toxic confusional states) which may be produced by physical factors such as infections, toxins, hypoglycaemia, hypothermia, etc. Such states are typified by a "clouding of consciousness".

1. There is disorientation as to time, place and person (usually in that order).

2. Anxiety and restlessness are produced by the above.

3. Defects of concentration and attention are present.

4. Patients often have fluctuating paranoid ideas.

5. Hallucinations (typically visual) are often experienced.

6. The symptoms bear no relationship to the pre-morbid personality.

7. The symptoms are often worse at night.

Treatment should be aimed at the underlying organic cause, not at the resultant psychological symptoms. Most cases will then recover to the pre-morbid level but permanent brain damage is possible.

Thus such disorders rarely require compulsory treatment in a psychiatric hospital but their florid symptoms frequently give rise to referrals to doctors, psychiatrists and ASWs as acute psychiatric emergencies.

18

B. Chronic

Dementia, or chronic brain failure, may be defined as an irreversible decline in brain function which may be due to pathology within the brain itself, "intrinsic brain failure", e.g. caused by atrophy, disease, cerebral atherosclerosis or to pathology elsewhere in the body, "extrinsic brain failure", e.g. due to chronic heart or lung disease which reduces blood supply to the brain. It should be noted that particular infections, such as AIDS and Creuzfeld-Jakob Disease, can produce dementia at an atypical age.

There are two main types of chronic brain failure, both associated with ageing.

(a) **Senile Dementia**
(otherwise referred to as Alzheimer Type Brain Failure or Senile Dementia, Alzheimer Type-SDAT.)

1. It runs a slow progressive course.

2. The damage is irreversible.

3. Memory impairment is marked, especially the memory for recent events.

4. There is loss of the powers of concentration and attention. Such losses may produce perseveration (the reiteration of questions, statements, etc.)

5. There may be a flattening of expressed emotion or a loss of emotional control.

6. Irritability is often marked.

7. There may be a breakdown in social controls, e.g. in eating habits, of sexual inhibitions, etc.

8. Patients may become restless and wander off.

9. Behaviour frequently becomes attention-seeking.

10. There may be marked agitation and anxiety.

11. Sleep disturbance is common and there may be sleep reversal, i.e. sleeping by day and wakeful at night.

12. The patient may become suspicious of others and may accuse them of theft, poisoning, etc.

13. Diffuse brain damage tends to affect all aspects of the personality.

Treatment is aimed at maintaining a good standard of general health which may help to slow down the inevitable deterioration. In this, a well-balanced diet, attention to bowel habits, treatment of minor ailments and infections, sufficient warmth, etc., are all important.

The usual aim is to maintain the client in his own familiar environment for as long as possible. In this, the roles of the social worker, district nurse, home help, meals on wheels, day care services, etc., are crucial. It may be possible to enlist the help of relatives, neighbours and voluntary agencies who may be more willing to supplement professional support services than they would be to shoulder the whole burden. Short-term residential placement may be invaluable to help the family, but it may exacerbate the client's symptoms for a while. As far as possible, a fixed routine in the client's day-to-day life may help him cope better. Reality Orientation Therapy may be of value.

Drugs which dilate cerebral blood vessels are available but, while there is some evidence that they may lead to an improvement in the patient's performance in psychological tests, there is little clinical evidence of their value in the underlying brain failure.

A similar clinical picture may be seen in rather younger patients. This is known as "pre-senile dementia" or Alzheimer's Disease.

There is a voluntary organisation, the Alzheimer's Disease Society, which provides much useful information for patients and those caring for them.

(b) Multi-Infarct Brain Failure
(M.I.B.F. or Athero-Sclerotic Dementia)

1. The condition is associated with pathology of the main arteries and a resultant raised blood pressure.

2. Smaller arteries in the brain become blocked, resulting in scattered areas of brain damage (infarctions).

3. Symptoms develop rapidly and their nature and the resultant loss of brain function depend on the site and extent of the damage. Other areas of brain functioning are left more or less intact.

4. Thus the picture is of a patchy step-like deterioration of brain functioning affecting some but not all aspects of personality and cerebral processes.

5. Physical symptoms such as loss of vision, hearing, movement, speech, etc., may occur if the areas of brain controlling them are affected.

Functional Psychoses

The aetiology of these mental disorders is still unknown. Theories range from faulty family relationships to as yet unidentified or unproven biochemical abnormality. No brain lesion or any other pathological process has so far been demonstrated sufficiently clearly to establish a definite cause. Nevertheless the functions of the mind are disturbed and the resultant effects can be described and classified. They can be described under two main headings, affective disorders and schizophrenia. For reasons of clarity, schizophrenia will be dealt with in sections six and seven.

21

Affective Disorders

These relate to the mood or emotion displayed by the individual.

Manic-Depressive Psychosis

The incidence of this condition is about 2% in males and 3% in females. Typically, it first occurs at about middle-age, but can begin earlier.

There tends to be a family history and pattern of the condition and classically it is more common in the "pyknic" body type. Such people tend to be stocky, with large trunks, short necks and limbs.

It may be "bi-polar" i.e. marked by episodes of mania in one attack, of depression in another; or "unipolar" i.e. each episode is of mania or each is of depression. The depressed phase is called "endogenous depression", i.e. it appears to develop spontaneously from within the individual without any identifiable outside cause. With either pattern, there are intervening periods of normality but there is a tendency for these to become shorter as the individual becomes older. Depression is more common than mania.

Endogenous Depression

1. The depression appears to develop from within the individual and is not precipitated by any apparent external cause.

2. At first the patient may not complain of feeling depressed, but of a loss of interest, energy, etc.

3. As the condition develops, the individual may complain of feelings of sadness and of being unable to shake off a mood of melancholy.

4. As the depression deepens, there may be feelings of hopelessness.

22

5. The mood tends to fluctuate a little during the day, being rather more depressed in the morning and lifting a little towards evening.

6. The patient does not improve in company and may in fact feel worse.

7. The sleep pattern tends to be disturbed. Typically it is fairly easy to get off to sleep but the patient wakes very early, beset with anxiety and deeply depressed.

8. The appetite tends to be lost and consequently there is also weight loss.

9. Commonly, there are complaints of vague somatic symptoms such as headache, backache, indigestion, etc. Menstruation may cease.

10. Constipation is common.

11. These "biological" symptoms frequently cause fears of a physical illness such as cancer. Such fears may develop into "nihilistic delusions" of the body's organs rotting, disappearing, etc.

12. Psycho-motor retardation is present, i.e. a slowing down of mental and physical activity. This can develop to such an extent that a depressive stupor may occur.

13. There may be ruminations and delusions of sin, guilt and punishment. They may often concern earlier sexual activities such as masturbation, or some real or imagined minor transgression.

14. In older people, these symptoms may be accompanied by a marked restlessness and agitation - "involutional melancholia"

15. The risk of suicide is high, both as depression deepens and early in treatment when retardation is reduced but depression remains profound.

Cause

As yet no clear cause has been identified. There is evidence of bio-chemical abnormalities affecting the transmission of impulses along nerve fibres and between nerves, but the causal connection is not yet proved.

Course

Without treatment the natural course of this condition is a return to normality over a period of about 2-3 years. It tends to recur. Suicide is always a risk.

Treatment

Because of the very real risk of suicide and the lack of insight into his condition on the part of the patient, and the risk to the patient's general health, treatment may need to be in hospital, if necessary on a compulsory basis.

Drugs

These fall into three main groups:

(a) Mono-amine oxidase inhibitors (MAOI's) such as *Nardil, Parnate or Parstelin*. They all require that the patient avoids taking many other drugs and does not eat such foods as bananas, cheese, yeast extracts, broad beans, game meat, and does not drink alcohol.

(b) Tri-cyclics such as *Tofranil, Tryptizol and Concordin*. There are no dietary restrictions but they may produce side-effects such as a dry mouth, blurred vision, retention of urine, etc. These often tend to diminish as the treatment continues.

(c) Lithium salts such as *Priadel*. These are used to reduce the frequency of episodes of recurrent depression (and mania).

Anti-depressant drugs, though effective, do not begin to take effect until after about 10 days or more. They must be taken regularly, often for a long period of time. Any dietary restrictions must be observed, and any side-effects reported to the prescribing doctor.

24

ECT – Electro-Convulsive Therapy or Electroplexy

An electric current is passed across the patient's brain. This may be across the frontal lobes, or the current may be passed from the front to the back of one side only. Nowadays it is almost invariably done after the patient has been given a short-acting general anaesthetic and a muscle relaxant. Together these reduce the former "convulsion" to a slight twitching of the muscles in the face and a spasm in the fingers and toes.

ECT may be given on an outpatient basis. A typical course consists of one to three doses per week to a total of about 6-12 applications, though this varies according to the severity of the symptoms and the individual's response. Some patients may receive a "maintenance" dose at considerable intervals of time.

In normal circumstances the patient must consent to ECT. However, under Section 58 of the Act, it may be given in cases where the patient cannot or does not consent, subject to a second medical opinion. In urgent cases, the treatment may be started pending a second opinion.

Although the precise mode of action of ECT has not been established and thus its use can be and is attacked, many doctors maintain that it is safe and works more quickly than drugs. It can thus be life-saving. Recent studies have suggested a strong placebo effect but have demonstrated the benefit of treatment especially in retarded and deluded patients.

There is little doubt that many recipients of ECT experience headache and some memory loss after treatment. However, it should be remembered that a depressive illness may itself affect memory.

Opinions differ as to the permanence of memory defect following ECT and on whether applications of the electrodes to one rather than both sides of the head reduces memory impairment.

Mania

The underlying cause remains unknown. Freudian theory sees mania as a flight from depression. Others postulate a biochemical disturbance affecting nerve function.

Mania is less common than depression and its prognosis tends to be worse. The first attack tends to occur later in life, after the age of about 35.

(Hypomania is a less severe form of the condition, sharing similar though milder symptoms, as below, but without delusions or hallucinations.)

1. The individual becomes excited, elated and over-active mentally and physically.

2. He may be euphoric but may find the experience unpleasant and frightening.

3. In the earlier stages of the condition, the patient may be very plausible and carry others along in his enthusiasm.

4. The rate of speech becomes accelerated; new words may be invented. Speech may degenerate into a "word salad".

5. He may exhibit a "flight of ideas" in which he switches rapidly from one subject to another. There is often only a tenuous connection between each successive idea.

6. Irritability is marked, especially in response to frustration or the apparent stupidity of other people. This may develop into aggression.

7. The sleep pattern is disturbed. Little sleep seems to be needed.

8. Libido may be increased.

9. Irresponsible or anti-social behaviour may occur.

10. Although the patient may expend great energy, it is often unproductive and dissipated by the high level of distractibility.

11. Delusions may develop, typically of a grandiose or religiose nature.

12. Hallucinations of a similar nature to the delusions may occur.

Social consequences may be severe for the patient and his family. For example, he may incur debts, strain inter-personal relationships, commit offences, lose or leave employment, etc.

Treatment

Because of the nature of their illness, manic patients tend to be unco-operative with treatment. Compulsory admission to hospital may be needed.

Drugs used are usually the "major tranquillisers", such as *Largactil or Triperidol*. As with the depressive phase, Lithium salts such as *Priadel* may reduce the frequency and severity of attacks or terminate a manic episode.

ECT may be used. It does sometimes have a tranquillising effect and may damp down or extinguish delusions.

Six

Schizophrenia

It is perhaps more accurate to think of this as a group of related disorders, rather than as a single entity. Of all the psychoses, schizophrenia provokes the most controversy as to cause, prognosis, treatment, etc.

Laing suggest that it is the result of faulty family relationships. Another theory is that of the "schizophrenogenic mother" who holds her child in a series of double-bind situations from which he retreats into illness. Some sociologists suggest a cause which lies in the anomie of inner-city slums. The medical model suggests an as yet unknown biochemical basis.

Schizophrenia is not the "split personality" of fiction, such as "Dr Jekyll and Mr Hyde", though this is a commonly held lay belief. It affects a little under one per cent of the population and this figure remains fairly constant in all societies and cultures provided that the same diagnostic criteria are used.

There tends to be a history of mental illness and abnormality among the families of schizophrenics, though the illness does not fit either the dominant or recessive gene pattern. There is a high correlation rate in studies of identical twins even when they are reared apart.

The prognosis of schizophrenia is variable. Of newly diagnosed cases, about one-third may be expected to make a good recovery, another third to improve, and the remaining third to make poor progress with a significant rate of chronicity.

In the present state of medical knowledge, treatment is aimed at removing target symptoms. At this level it may be successful, but the underlying disease process, whatever this may be, is not cured.

28

Schizophrenia has some relationship to body build, being more common in the "aesthenic" type, i.e. people who tend to be thin, poorly muscled with poor peripheral circulation leading to cold, blue extremities. When it occurs in such a person, the prognosis tends to be worse than in other body types.

The rapidity of the first onset may be significant. There seems to be a more hopeful prognosis where the condition develops rapidly in an individual whose previous personality was reasonably well integrated, rather than where it seems to grow slowly out of a previously "schizoid" personality, i.e. shy, introverted, ill at ease with new situations and relationships.

Previous inter-personal relationships may be important. Schizophrenia in an individual with a stable, well-adjusted family background or a stable marriage carries a better prognosis.

Many schizophrenics are found to be dependent on elderly relatives, often widowed mothers, who in turn seem to depend upon the patient for company and a reason for living. Such relatives may be somewhat unco-operative in the patient's treatment as they have a vested interest in his sick role.

It is predominantly an illness which begins in late adolescence or early adult life, hence the earlier term "dementia praecox". The earlier the onset, the greater tends to be the damage to personality.

Typically schizophrenics experience great difficulty in forming or maintaining close personal relationships. Often they are unable to tolerate the emotional demands made upon them in such contexts. Such cases may fare better when day care facilities can be used to reduce the daily duration of these relationships. In the same way, life in the more neutral emotional climate of a hostel or group home may help them.

There are several types of schizophrenia which may be different, but closely related disease entities. Classification depends upon the predominance of certain symptoms and may be easier in the early stages of the condition.

All the types share certain symptoms in common, and these must be present at least to some extent in order for a safe diagnosis to be made. If sufficient evidence is lacking, terms such as "schizo-affective psychosis" or "schizophreniform psychosis" may be used.

The major symptoms of schizophrenia are:-

a disorder of   - affect (mood or emotions)
                - thought
                - volition (will)
The presence of - delusions (primary type)
                - hallucinations

Affective Disorder may take the form of "blunting", where there is little or no affective response, or "incongruity", where there is an inappropriate response.

Thought Disorder may take several different forms and more than one may be present at the same time.

"Thought Blocking" causes pauses in the patient's flow of speech as his train of thought is interrupted.

"Thought Implantation" means that the patient believes that other people are putting thoughts into his mind.

"Knight's Move Thinking" is a disorder in which thoughts on one subject are expressed, then interrupted, then followed by thoughts about a different but related subject.

"Thought Broadcasting" is the belief that thoughts are audible and shared by others.

The facility for abstract thought is lost, with a return to concrete thinking. There is an inability to differentiate and exclude irrelevant material from the patient's thoughts.

30

Volitional Disorder may be manifested as passivity, negativism or double orientation.

Primary Delusions appear in a fully developed form rather than developing gradually over a period of time. They tend to be topical and often have a pseudo-scientific flavour, e.g. concerned with radar, radio beams, space satellites, etc.

Hallucinations may be of any of the senses but typically they are auditory and take the form of voices which talk to or about the patient, often in a derogatory way. The voices often use figures of speech, such as rhymes, puns, play on words, etc.

Neurotic Overlay may be caused by the stress of the onset of the psychotic illness. Symptoms of depression, anxiety, obsessionality, etc., may be present and in the early stages may be more obvious than those of the underlying schizophrenia.

Types of Schizophrenia

1. Simple Schizophrenia

This tends to occur at adolescence and grows out of a pre-morbid personality which is shy, introverted, lonely, etc.

Affect is the primary disorder, becoming blunted or incongruous.

Thought disorder develops, taking one or more of the forms described above. The patient may show perplexity. There may be "ideas of reference" in which the patient believes that newspapers or television programmes contain hidden meanings or messages for him.

Volition, the will to do things, is often decreased and may be demonstrated by self-neglect, failure to attend school or work, failure to collect social security benefits, and so on. The patient may display passivity by leaving all decisions to others and obeying them completely. He may show negativism in a mute refusal to obey or by doing the opposite of what is asked. As the condition develops, delusions and hallucinations may occur.

31

N.B. It is important to differentiate between this condition and manifestations of adolescence.

2. Hebephrenic Schizophrenia - "youthful thinking"

This condition tends to occur a little later than the simple type, typically in the late teens.

Thought is the primary disorder and often the thought disorder is accompanied by a childish silliness and giggling.

Disorders of *affect and volition* follow a similar pattern to those described above, and delusions and hallucinations may develop.

3. Catatonic Schizophrenia

This occurs typically in the early twenties. **Volition** is the primary disorder, accompanied by a marked change in the tone of the muscles. This enables the patient's limbs and posture to be moulded into bizarre positions in which they will remain for long periods without apparent strain or fatigue. This ability to mould the body like warm wax is called *"flexibilitas cerea"*. The patient may enter a catatonic stupor in which he appears to be in a trance, but nevertheless remains aware of events in his environment. There may alternatively be a catatonic frenzy, a sudden outburst of excitability and hyperactivity. The other disorders of thought and affect are also present and, later, delusions and hallucinations.

4. Paranoid Schizophrenia

This tends to occur later in life than the types described above, typically in the thirties. It is much less related to body build than the other forms and, on the whole, leads to less total disintegration of the personality.

Delusions form the prime symptoms, typically of plots against the patient. He may believe that the police or spy rings are hunting him, that he has been maliciously and falsely accused of a crime, wrong-fully refused promotion, etc. In other cases the delusion may take a grandiose or religiose form.

Though the other first-rank symptoms are present, they tend to be much less severe (outside the delusional pattern) than in other forms of schizophrenia.

5. Paraphrenia - "schizophrenia of late onset"

This occurs among the older age group, after about 60-65 years of age, and more commonly in women.

Delusions predominate, often centred around neighbours, etc. They may have a highly charged sexual content. Often the old person is deeply suspicious of callers and may refuse to open the door to them. The door may have been fitted with several locks, bolts and chains. Window curtains remain closed and letter boxes are blocked. Accusations of theft may be made against social workers, home helps, district nurses, etc., who visit and social contacts tend to be avoided.

Outside the delusional system the patient may be able to cope with life, but often provokes anxiety among neighbours and welfare agencies because of the hermit-like lifestyle, accusations and refusals of help which are regarded as malicious interference.

Treatment

At present this can only be aimed at target symptoms. Drugs are widely used with a heavy emphasis on the "major tran-quillisers". *Largactil* was the first of these and is still used in many cases, though there are many similar and popular drugs. Taken in high doses over a long period, they may all produce side-effects such as drowsiness, weight-gain and symptoms similar to those of Parkinson's Disease. This last may necessitate the use of anti-Parkinsonian drugs such as *Disipal or Artane.*

Physical side-effects such as uncontrollable movements of the mouth and tongue, the inability to sit or stand still and a "pill-rolling" tremor of the fingers may occur early or late after treatment - *"tardive dyskinesia"*. Its onset appears to be related to the dosage and duration of treatment. Older patients seem to be particularly at risk.

33

A common feature of schizophrenia is an unreliability in taking medication regularly. In order to combat this, and avoid the resurgence of acute symptoms, many patients are given injections of long-acting drugs at two or three weekly intervals. Such drugs include *Modecate* and they are often given at outpatient clinics or by community nurses. The same side-effects may occur as with oral medication; tablets to avoid these may still be necessary.

Psychotherapy with an individual patient is little used except as a supportive measure. Occupational or industrial therapy may be very useful in extending the patient's attention span, for example, in rehabilitation.

"Burning Out"

As the duration of the illness increases and the patient ages, his symptoms may become much less florid. Patients tend not to express their delusional ideas or react to hallucinations. Often they become emotionally blunted, manneristic, rather unkempt individuals who may display odd or stereotyped behaviour. This is accompanied by the effects of institutionalisation and often the side-effects of long-term treatment.

Many of the "chronic graduates" are like this, i.e. patients who developed schizophrenia before the advent of satisfactory treatment and have grown old in our mental hospitals. In recent years, large numbers have been discharged, often to group homes, hostels, or bed-sits.

Seven

Social Work with Schizophrenics

Schizophrenics should not be thought of or treated as a group entity. Despite sharing an illness, they remain individuals, each with his own problems and needs. However, some common principles do emerge.

In the early acute stages of the condition, the social worker may be involved at a crisis point. She may be faced with a frightened family who cannot cope with its schizophrenic member. The client himself may be depressed or frightened in a world which no longer makes sense to him and over which he is rapidly losing control. In such circumstances the social worker may often need to reassure and support the family. At the same time she may need to involve herself in the referral, admission or removal of the client to hospital.

As a general rule, aggression and violence are not major components of schizophrenia, though impulsive behaviour is common. In many cases the client can be persuaded to do what is wanted rather than being forced. Many a Napoleon, interrupted en route to Waterloo, will accompany the social worker quite docilely to see a doctor first.

If compulsion is used, then it must be unavoidable in the circumstances prevailing at the time and must be within the legal context of the Mental Health Act 1983. If used, then it must be used sensibly, carefully and caringly. Although they may be mentally ill, schizophrenics are not usually stupid and will generally accept the inevitability of bowing to superior numbers. There is no disgrace in a social worker seeking additional help to remove a client, rather than attempting to struggle with him alone.

In the interests of the client and his family, such help should be asked to arrive at the scene discreetly, unaccompanied by blaring sirens or flashing lights.

A compulsory admission to hospital should not be seen as an insuperable obstacle to further involvement or relationship between worker and client. It is simply a course of action that has to be done at that time (or else it should not be done) and which has to be worked through later when the crisis has passed. Much greater and more lasting damage to future work can be done by a social worker who avoids compulsion by using lies to "con" her client.

In the later stages of schizophrenia, social work involvement is usually aimed at supporting the family, reducing any harmful dependency situations between client and relatives, and rehabilitating the client. This last may present considerable difficulty in view of the prejudice towards the mentally ill on the part of some relatives, neighbours, employers, etc.

Aftercare of a mentally ill client cannot ignore the medical aspects of the case. The worker may need to liaise with other professionals such as the psychiatrist, general practitioner or community psychiatric nurse. It is necessary to pay attention to any medication being taken by the client and to develop some understanding of its effects and possible side-effects. It is important to encourage the client to keep outpatient appointments.

There are special problems when working with chronic schizophrenics who have been returned to the community after many years in a mental hospital. Many are so institutionalised that an independent life is almost impossible for them. In addition to the damage done to their personality by the illness, they have spent many years in an environment which has actively discouraged the use of any residual initiative they may have, has often prevented normal contact with the outside world and has met all their needs from within its own resources. Even such trivia as turning off lights and fires, making a cup of tea or buying essentials may have to be re-learned. The steps taken by the hospital to rehabilitate such patients before discharging them may be excellent, but this is not so in all cases.

It may be necessary to consider group homes, hostels or old people's homes rather than leaving them to fend for themselves in a community which may be alien and uncaring.

It may be very helpful to enlist the aid of voluntary agencies, such as local associations of MIND, in caring for such clients. Much useful information about the condition can be obtained from the National Schizophrenia Fellowship.

Section 117 of the Act imposes a duty to provide aftercare, for as long as it is needed, on district health and social services authorities in respect of patients discharged from detention for treatment. This should include multi-disciplinary planning for the patient's discharge and the formulation of a care plan for him in the light of resources and facilities available, e.g. accommodation, day care, opportunities for rehabilitation, occupation, recreation and socialisation. A key worker, e.g. a social worker or community psychiatric nurse, should be nominated to implement the agreed plan and to liaise with other professionals and volunteers. The key worker should monitor the patient's progress and report back to the pre-discharge team so that the plan can be modified if necessary.

Schizophrenia may lead to long-term problems. For example, relatives may equate discharge from hospital with cure and have unrealistic expectations that the patient will be able to resume his pre-morbid role in the family and in society. This may lead to demands being made upon him which he cannot meet, and thus to a resurgence of symptoms. The social worker may need to help relatives accept a greater or lesser degree of handicap in the patient, and to adjust their roles and expectations.

The schizophrenic may experience difficulty in employment. In situations which require the use of initiative, motivation and thought, the illness may have impaired these abilities. In routine, repetitive jobs, the patient's limited attention span may lead to poor performance.

Eight
Mental Handicap or Mental Impairment?

The definition of mental disorder contained in Part I of the Mental Health Act 1983 means that the vast majority of people with learning disabilities are not subject to compulsory powers in respect of treatment or guardianship for which a classification of mental impairment or severe mental impairment is required.

If appropriate, they may be admitted to hospital compulsorily for assessment. They may also suffer from other forms of mental disorder, i.e. mental illness or psychopathic disorder.

The first biennial Report of the Mental Health Act Commission expresses concern that their removal from the definition of mental disorder has also removed them from the overview of the Commission and that "there is no automatic access to the benign statutory effects such as the manager's duty to explain to the patient his rights, overview by the Commission, second opinion on treatment, appeal and automatic reference to the Mental Health Review Tribunal and entitlement to jointly organised aftercare".

The report also expresses concern about children and young persons in mental handicap and mental illness hospitals. It points out that it is rare for them to be admitted compulsorily under the Act if under 16. Admissions are more usually by means of a Care Order with a Juvenile Court making a Hospital or Guardianship Order. Such patients have none of the protection available under the Mental Health Act. They tend to get "lost in the system"; having been "volunteered" by parents or guardians at an early age, they remain as "voluntary" patients for the rest of their lives; and in some places their care and treatment receive a low priority.

The Code of Practice offers guidance as to the differentiation between handicap and impairment.

It states that "arrested or incomplete development of mind" implies that the handicap has been present from the stage which has permanently prevented the usual maturation of intellectual and social development. It excludes those handicapped by accident, injury or illness occurring after the usually accepted point of complete development.

The diagnosis is a matter for clinical judgment but the World Health Organisation classification may be a useful guide.

Category	WHO I.Q. Range	M.H.A. 1983
Average	85-115	Nil
Dull Normal	70-84	Slight
Mild	50-69	Significant
Moderate	35-49)	
Severe	20-34)	Severe
Profound	<19)	

The Code of Practice points out the importance of communication in the assessment process, e.g. by someone known to the subject, or through Makaton, etc. The level of intelligence and of social functioning should be assessed by an experienced multi-disciplinary team.

This form of assessment should also be used where admission is being considered under Section 2 on grounds of "arrested or incomplete development of mind" unless the urgency of the situation prevents it.

"Abnormally aggressive conduct" should be categorised by reference to observations of the patient's behaviour which lead to the conclusion that it is outside the usually accepted range of aggressive behaviour which causes actual damage and/or real distress occurring recently, persistently or with excessive severity. Such behaviour is mostly unpredictable and severe, e.g. damaging others by physical acts or throwing objects to cause damage to others.

Such behaviour should be recent. However, for some people, infrequent but seriously aggressive behaviour constitutes their dangerousness and consequently grounds for detention.

The actual conduct should if possible have been observed in behavioural terms, preferably by at least two reliable witnesses.

"Irresponsible conduct" should be based on observations which show its lack of responsibility, a disregard for its consequences and which results in actual damage or real distress, either recently or persistently or with excessive severity. Such conduct frequently constitutes a serious or potentially serious danger, where the person concerned does not show appropriate regard to its consequences e.g. absconding, arson, life-endangering self-neglect.

Doctors should encourage the courts to use powers under Sections 35, 36 and 38 (q.v.) to assess and ameliorate the disorder rather than using a Hospital Order (Section 37).

Social services departments should formulate policies for the guardianship of mentally and severely mentally impaired patients as being the least restrictive alternative. Such policies should be made known to the courts.

Nine

Psychopathic Disorder

The Act distinguishes psychopathic disorder from mental illness. It is defined as "persistent disorder or disability of mind (whether or not including significant impairment of intelligence) which results in abnormally aggressive or seriously irresponsible conduct on the part of the person concerned".

Little is known with any certainty about the causes of psychopathy, though it has been recognised for many years. In the 1830's, Pritchard described "moral insanity" in which the patient was not clinically insane but exhibited behaviour disorders. The term "psychopath" was coined by Koch about 1890 to describe a degeneration of the personality. In continental Europe the term is used (e.g. by Schneider) in a broader sense to describe those whose personality makes themselves or society suffer.

Many psychiatrists try to avoid involvement with psychopaths on the grounds that there is no medical treatment. This view led to efforts to remove psychopathy from the Act. These were unsuccessful but the concept of the disorder's treatability in the 1959 Act's definition was removed, as were the age limits on admission and detention. However, in order for a patient to be admitted to hospital compulsorily for treatment of psychopathic disorder, a treatability criterion must be satisfied.

Symptoms

These vary considerably among individuals but certain traits are common.

1. An inability to learn from past experience.

2. Callousness, or at least an indifference to the rights and feelings of other people, and marked egocentricity.

3. The ability to manipulate others.

41

4. A lack of regard for truth, norms of behaviour, etc.

5. An ability to be charming if it suits the individual at the time.

6. A low tolerance for frustration.

7. A lack of emotional control.

8. A predilection to act impulsively.

The condition is much more common in males than in females, occurring in the ratio 8:1 and among the young rather than the old.

Cause

There is no generally agreed and accepted cause but theories fall into three main classes.

1. Genetic/Constitutional

Studies have shown that the majority of psychopaths come from families with other disturbed and/or criminal members. There is a high correlation in studies of identical twins. The disorder is persistent and of early onset.

The electro-encephalograph (EEG) of normal young children differs from that of normal adults. However, some psychopaths retain juvenile wave forms which may be evidence of brain immaturity.

2. Environmental

There is frequently a history of disturbed family relationships, especially of inconsistent parents. The condition could be the result of early brain damage or of a brain infection in childhood.

3. Cultural

Psychopathy could be the result of early deprivation acting upon some constitutional predisposition.

Effects

The disorder may be classified on the basis of behavioural symptoms:-

(a) *The aggressive psychopath* tends to react violently to frustration and often has a long history of assaults, wife and child abuse, heavy drinking, etc.

(b) *The inadequate psychopath* seems unable to come to terms with society's rules and expectations. They are often heavily in debt, with a history of evictions, withdrawal of gas and electricity supplies, etc. They may be petty, and usually inefficient, criminals and often know nothing of contraception, child-rearing, etc.

(c) *The creative psychopath*, in the pursuit of his masterpiece, allows his wife and children to starve.

Treatment

Traditional medical treatment is usually quite ineffective. The use of medication often results in drug abuse, over-dosing and so on. Many doctors suggest that the penal system should deal with these individuals, but this is no more effective and the recidivism rate among psychopaths is high.

Long term re-education and resocialisation along group lines in a therapeutic community is being used in some areas and claims promising results.

Social work with clients who are suffering from a psychopathic disorder is often beset with problems. These stem from the client's inherent unreliability, his manipulative ability and the common lack of enthusiastic support from other workers.

These problems are usually made more manageable if involvement is limited to one social worker. This enables her to get to know the client, reduces the opportunities for manipulation and allows an integrated "treatment" plan to be attempted.

43

Ten
The Approved Social Worker

The local social services authority has a duty to appoint a sufficient number of Approved Social Workers (ASWs) to carry out its functions under the Act. *(Section 114(1))*

Before appointing an ASW, the local authority must have regard to such directions as the Secretary of State may give. *(Section 114(3))*

Those appointed must have "appropriate competence in dealing with persons suffering from mental disorder". *(Section 114(2))*

When appointed, the ASW has many functions and powers.

1. As applicant, the ASW will take the patient to hospital and has the power to authorise others to do this on her behalf. *Section 6(1)*

2. Before or within a reasonable time after making an application for assessment (Section 2), the ASW must take such steps as are practicable to inform the patient's nearest relative of the application and of the nearest relative's right to seek the patient's discharge under Section 23(2)(a). *Section 11(3)*

3. The ASW has an obligation to consult the patient's nearest relative before making an application for treatment (Section 3) or for guardianship unless such consultation would involve unreasonable delay or is not reasonably practicable. The ASW may not proceed if the nearest relative objects. *Section 11(4)*

4. The ASW has a duty to make application for admission to hospital or guardianship in respect of a patient within the area of her employing authority if she is satisfied that such an application ought to be made by her. *Section 13(1)*

44

5. Before making an application, the ASW must interview the patient in a suitable manner. *Section 13(2)*

6. An ASW may make application outside the area of her local authority. *Section 13(3)*

7. If so required by the patient's nearest relative, the local social services authority shall direct an ASW as soon as practicable to take a patient's case into consideration with a view to making an application for his admission to hospital. If the ASW decides not to make application, she shall inform the nearest relative of her reasons in writing. *Section 13(4)*.

She should also inform the doctors making the medical recommendations.

She need not supply the appropriate forms but the Code of Practice suggests that it is good practice for the ASW to consider whether to advise the nearest relative of his or her own right to make the application and if this is exercised how far the ASW should assist, especially in removing the patient.

The ASW's minimum obligation is to advise the nearest relative to seek medical advice about the patient's possible admission, to tell him or her about the necessary procedures and sources of assistance in taking the patient to hospital and to consider what continuing social work help is needed by the family.

8. Where a patient is admitted to hospital on application by his nearest relative (except under Section 4), a social worker will be required to supply a social circumstances report to the hospital managers. *Section 14*

9. The ASW has power to retake and return a patient absent without leave from hospital or guardianship. *Section 18*

10. The ASW has power to apply to a County Court to appoint an acting nearest relative. *Section 29(2)*

11. The ASW may be directed by the court making a Hospital Order to convey the patient to hospital. *Section 40*

12. The ASW has power to retake and return any patient absent without leave from a hospital in Northern Ireland. *Section 87.* Similar powers are conferred in respect of patients absent without leave from Scottish hospitals by the Mental Health (Scotland) Act, 1984.

13. The ASW has power to retake and return any patient absent without leave from a hospital in the Channel Islands or Isle of Man. *Section 89*

14. The ASW has power to enter and inspect any premises (not being a hospital) in the area of her local authority in which a mentally disordered person is living if she has reasonable cause to believe that the patient is not under proper care. *Section 115*

15. The duty of the local social services authority and district health authority to provide aftercare for certain patients may devolve to the ASW. *Section 117*

16. The ASW has power to obtain a magistrate's warrant authorising the police to enter premises in which a person suffering from mental disorder is being ill-treated, neglected or kept otherwise than under proper control or, being unable to care for himself, is living alone. The ASW must accompany the police. *Section 135(1)*

17. The ASW (among others) has power to obtain a magistrate's warrant to enable the police to enter premises and retake and return a patient absent without leave. The ASW may accompany the police. *Section 135(2)*

18. The ASW has a duty to interview patients removed to a Place of Safety by the police. *Section 136(2)*

46

19. The ASW has all the powers, authorities, protection and privileges of a constable when taking, conveying or detaining a compulsorily detained patient. *Section 137(2)*

20. The ASW has power to retake patients who escape while being conveyed to any place. *Section 138(1)*

It is clear from Section 13 of the Act that the ASW's duties and powers in respect of applications under Part II are personal ones. While consultation with and advice from senior colleagues may be appropriate or helpful, ultimately that decision rests with the individual ASW.

Provided that the ASW does not act in bad faith or without reasonable care, she is protected from civil proceedings, except with the leave of the High Court, and from criminal proceedings without the consent of the Director of Public Prosecutions. *(Section 139)*

Some Elements of the Social Work Task

DHSS Circular LAC(83)7 states:

ASWs should have a wider role than reacting to requests for admission to hospital, making the necessary arrangements and ensuring compliance with the law. They should have the specialist knowledge and skills to make appropriate decisions in respect of both clients and their relatives and to gain the confidence of colleagues in the health service with whom they are required to co-operate. They must be familiar with the day to day working of an integrated mental health service and be able to assess what other services may be required from the Social Services Department and elsewhere and know how to mobilise them. They should have access to, consultation with and supervision from qualified and experienced senior officers. Their role is to prevent the necessity for compulsory admission to hospital as well as to make application where they decide this is appropriate.

47

It may be difficult for the ASW to reach the proper decision, especially when under pressure from doctors, relatives, police, etc., who may have a vested interest in the removal of the patient to hospital. The difficulties are compounded if the ASW does not know the patient, is unable to gain access to his records, if any, and has little confidence in her own role and expertise. The decision-making process is not helped if the ASW has reason to believe that her management will fail to support her.

Problems may occur most frequently outside normal office hours and crises are often precipitated or made worse by the actions of other agencies. For example, a locum doctor who does not know the patient may recommend his admission and the duty consultant may be unable or unwilling to come out. The police may wish to dispose of an allegedly mentally disordered person and exert considerable pressure on the ASW. Inexperienced junior doctors on duty at accident and emergency departments may wish to pass the buck.

Work with mentally disordered clients, especially with those who are exhibiting florid symptoms, bizarre, disinhibited, aggressive, destructive or unpredictable behaviour, is often at a time of crisis and tends to provoke a high level of anxiety in those involved. Such anxiety is likely to be present in professionals as well as in the client himself and his relatives. It may be heightened by prejudice and stigmatisation, lack of knowledge and experience and the fear, which may be reasonable, that the client may harm himself or others. It is important that the ASW should recognise her own reactions to the situation in order to prevent them from colouring her perceptions and possibly affecting her judgment.

It is difficult to lay down hard and fast guidelines for social work intervention as in any situation there are variables associated with the client, his needs, available resources, etc. and different social workers may prefer to adopt particular strategies. However, some general principles may be cited.

A. The Referral

Where this is made by the patient's nearest relative, the local social services authority has a duty to send an ASW as soon as practicable to interview the patient with a view to making an application for his admission to hospital. It is suggested that the same response should be made if it is known that a doctor has made a medical recommendation for the patient's admission or intends to do so or if the ASW receives information from other sources that grounds may exist for an application to be made.

The Act does not specify a time limit for the ASW's response, except that it should be as soon as practicable. In the event, considerable time may be saved if the ASW defers her visit to the patient in order to consult case records, speak to the general practitioner, perhaps arrange a joint visit and, if appropriate, contact the hospital and the relevant consultant to establish the availability of a bed, the possibility of a domiciliary consultation and any other helpful information. For the ASW to arrive on the scene armed with as much information as possible often enables her to reassure others involved as well as helping to allay her own anxiety.

If it seems likely that the patient may be resistive or aggressive or likely to abscond or be otherwise difficult to interview (e.g. because of language differences), it is much easier for the ASW to obtain assistance from a colleague, interpreter or other agency before leaving the office than after having arrived at the site of the problem. If without such assistance, once inside the patient's home, the ASW may find it difficult to leave again in order to make such arrangements. There is no shame in requesting help, providing it is used discreetly and caringly. Such help can more easily be sent away with a word of thanks than obtained when struggling with a patient on one's own or when it may be inappropriate to leave the patient or telephones may be difficult to find.

It is helpful if the ASW has a sufficient supply of the statutory forms which are likely to be needed. Reliance should not be placed on doctors to carry forms for medical recommendations with them and if errors are made in the completion of the forms, it is easier to have them amended or replaced on the spot.

B. The Assessment

Within the area of her employing local authority, the ASW who has reasonable cause for concern about the welfare of a mentally disordered person has the right, at any reasonable time, after showing her credentials if asked to do so, to enter and inspect any premises (other than a hospital) in which a patient is living and is believed not to be under proper care. *(Section 115)* If anyone prevents such entry and inspection, such obstruction may constitute an offence. *(Section 129)* However, the ASW has no power to force entry and ultimately may need to use the provisions of Section 135.

The first practical problem which may arise is how the ASW is going to introduce herself, explain her presence and gain access to the patient. It is not always the case that patients are expecting the arrival of an ASW, understand her functions or welcome her intervention. They are unlikely to believe that she "just happened to call" and may be alienated if her approach is perceived as a threat. The Code of Practice requires the ASW to identify herself to the patient, his family and other professionals present and to explain her role and purpose. She should also ensure that the other professionals have done likewise.

The Act requires the ASW to "interview the patient in a suitable manner. *(Section 13(2))* The patient should be given the opportunity of being interviewed without other persons present but:

- if he is likely to behave in an unpredictable or violent manner a third person, preferably not a relative, should remain;

- if this is impossible and the ASW cannot interview the patient on his own, a relative should remain;
- the patient should be told why the professionals are there and the reasons why medical advice has been sought. At this stage, compulsory admission should not be mentioned;
- informal admission should be discussed.

It may be necessary to use an interpreter, e.g. because the patient has an inadequate command of English or is prelingually deaf. Such an interpreter should be chosen with care and preferably arranged in advance. If possible he or she should be familiar with the terminology to be used. Relatives should only be used as a last resort.

Interviews through locked doors and windows should be avoided if at all possible.

In the case of mute or unresponsive patients, the ASW must do her best to obtain and impart information. This may be supplemented by information obtained from any other available source but its relevance and reliability must be weighed carefully.

If the patient is sedated, it may be preferable to defer an assessment of his condition until the effects have diminished. If this is not possible, e.g. because the patient's condition is likely to be too disturbed, the ASW may have to rely on information from others. Careful recording of the interview will be required.

In relation to the patient himself, the ASW should consider:

(a) the extent of the patient's insight and self-awareness where he is seeking to reject medical advice:

(b) any available medical, nursing or social work records:

(c) types of treatment or accommodation likely to be available on admission, e.g. from the ASW's own knowledge or from enquiries from the hospital.

51

If a decision is made to admit the patient, the doctor and ASW should consult together about information to be given to the patient and his relatives about (b) above. Things which may not happen are best not mentioned.

Wherever possible, a decision to admit a patient compulsorily should be a multi-disciplinary matter. Doctors and ASWs should explain their opinions and reasons openly to each other, to the patient and to the family.

Deception and subterfuge may only be used where they are clearly unavoidable and wholly necessary, e.g. when telling the patient the truth would result in a dangerous situation for him or others.

Doctors and ASWs should recognise that each has a specific role and duty. Each has the right and duty to form an independent opinion. Differences are inevitable and provide a safeguard for the patient if properly handled.

Both the doctor and the ASW must be satisfied that detention in a hospital is the most appropriate solution. The ASW need not question the doctor's finding of mental disorder but she can question the appropriateness of compulsory admission. She has a duty "to take into account all the circumstances of the case", i.e.

- other possible, less restrictive, methods of treatment available to meet the patient's need for treatment identified by the doctor;
- the views and wishes of the family;
- the best interests of the family;
- the danger or nuisance of the patient to the public;
- the burden of such other methods of treatment on the family or public;
- whether the patient will co-operate;
- whether guardianship would be appropriate.

Thus the ASW may also need to assess the patient's condition in the light of his past and present history, family situation and social circumstances, whether further material information may become available shortly, whether it is possible to postpone action pending this, etc.

Any delay must be weighed against possible risk to the patient, his relatives or others.

C. Obligations to Patients' Relatives (See also Chapter 11)

The nearest relative has the right to refer the patient's case to the local social services authority so that an ASW can assess the need for admission to hospital. It is suggested that the same response should be made to referrals by the nearest relative through a third party. If the ASW decides that admission is not appropriate, reasons must be given in writing to the nearest relative.

For admissions for assessment, the views of the patient's relatives should be taken into account by the ASW, though they are not binding. The ASW must inform the patient's nearest relative that an application for admission is being or has been made, and that relative must be told of his or her power to seek the patient's discharge. This does not mean that the ASW must make exhaustive efforts to contact and interview the nearest relative before the patient is admitted but, if such contact does not cause undesirable delay, it is preferable. If no such contact is made beforehand, it must be made later.

For admissions for treatment or guardianship, the ASW must contact and consult the nearest relative before the application is made unless this would involve unreasonable delay. Ideally, such applications should be pre-planned to allow full consultation to take place.

Considerable work may need to be done with an anxious and distressed relative to explain the patient's condition, support the relative, alleviate the consequences of the patient's disorder, etc., within the bounds of confidentiality to the patient. When the patient is ultimately discharged, the attitude of the nearest relative may be crucial to the patient's aftercare and long-term prospects.

D. Negotiations with Doctors

Relationships between doctors and ASWs can sometimes be difficult. Both parties must realise that their roles under the Act are different, complementary and equally important. Indeed, the whole basis of the Act is a multi-disciplinary, integrated approach. However, problems can arise when doctors and social workers use different concepts and models, employ different terminology and start from different bases of knowledge, training, experience and expectation. For example, the ASW is not required to have great expertise in clinical psychiatry, nor do most doctors have much knowledge of social work. It is when these differences arise in the context of a disturbed patient/client, anxious relatives, limited communication between professionals and unsureness as to their roles that conflict and confrontation may be produced.

The doctor's role is to examine the patient and, if appropriate, recommend his admission to hospital. He will also arrange a bed. The clinical diagnosis is the doctor's to make and it is usually unwise for the social worker to question it. However, the ASW is fully entitled to ask the doctor to justify the finding of mental disorder within the meaning of the Act and to explain the reasoning behind the diagnosis. The ASW can also query the need for compulsion and resist the inappropriate use of emergency powers.

The choice of whether to recommend admission under Section 2 (for assessment) or Section 3 (for treatment) rests mainly with the doctors concerned, though the views of the ASW may be sought. The Code of practice offers "pointers" to help in this choice.

Briefly, Section 2 may be preferred where the component of assessment predominates, where the patient may be able to become informal or where it is a first admission. Pointers to Section 3 are where the patient has needed longer term detention previously or where he is already detained under Section 2.

The decision should not be influenced by factors such as avoiding consultation with the Nearest Relative, that the treatment will last for less than 28 days or that the patient will have earlier recourse to a Tribunal under Section 2.

The ASW's role is to decide whether or not to apply for the patient's admission, and both aspects are equally important. The ASW has as great a duty to protect the patient from the inappropriate use of compulsory powers as to help in their use. She must satisfy herself that, in all the circumstances of the case, compulsory admission to hospital is the only way to meet the patient's needs. In her decision, medical opinion is obviously a very important factor, but it is not the sole factor by any means.

Doctors and ASWs should be prepared to share information, knowledge and experience, to answer each other's questions openly and to try to resolve any differences of opinion in the best interests of the patient. The whole process depends upon goodwill, honesty and respect for each other's position. Their discussions should take place out of the hearing and preferably the sight of the patient and his relatives. They have enough anxiety without witnessing what might become an argument between the professionals who are there to help them. Above all, the discussion should be kept on a professional level avoiding prejudices, stereotypes, threats or attempts to establish ascendancy.

If genuine disagreement persists, it should be seen as a protection for the patient, not a deliberate personal attack, obstruction or sabotage.

E. Decision not to Admit

If at the end of the assessment process the decision is made not to apply for the patient's compulsory admission, the professionals concerned should decide how to implement any alternative strategies and ensure that the patient and his relatives understand the situation.

The ASW must discuss with the Nearest Relative her reasons for not making an application (and give these in writing if the relative has referred the case to her) and should advise the Nearest Relative of his/her rights to make an application.

It should be remembered that there will be up to 14 days for valid medical recommendations to be based on the doctors' examinations.

F. The Removal

A duly completed set of "section documents" places the patient in the legal custody of the applicant who has all the powers of a constable. The applicant may delegate her powers to others who must then follow her directions. The patient remains in the custody of the applicant until the documents are received by an officer of the hospital so authorised by the managers.

Whenever possible the removal of the patient to hospital should be so planned as to be as unhurried and unobtrusive as possible. It may be appropriate for this to be done in the ASW's own car, perhaps with a colleague or the patient's relative as an escort. However, such methods are unlikely to succeed if the patient is resistive. Health authorities have a duty to provide ambulance transport for compulsory admissions and the ambulance crew may be directed by the applicant to help in the process, as a last resort using reasonable force. If force has to be used, it must be reasonable. The ASW should not hesitate to seek assistance from colleagues and/or the police rather than struggle with the patient and perhaps risk injury to herself or to the patient. In many cases, a patient will bow to the inevitable when faced with overwhelming numbers, and a sufficient number of people used to handling others makes a forcible removal less problematic if he does not. It may be appropriate for a doctor to give a small dose of a sedative to some patients but, if this involves a physical struggle, its value may need to be weighed against its possible risks. By and large, every attempt should be made to persuade the patient to go to hospital peacefully, even if this extends the time-scale of the removal. If all else fails and a forcible removal is unavoidable, then the anxiety level in everyone concerned will be raised considerably. The ASW may well need to return to reassure the patient's relatives afterwards. Considerable subsequent work may need to be done with the patient to restore the ASW's relationship with him if on-going work is to succeed.

The ASW may also need to make arrangements in respect of the patient's property, pets, etc., as part of her department's general responsibilities under the National Assistance Act 1948.

The Role of the ASW in Admissions

Before deciding on whether or not to apply for the patient's compulsory admission to hospital, the law requires the ASW to take a number of factors into consideration.

1. The ASW must interview the patient in "a suitable manner and satisfy herself that detention in a hospital is in all the circumstances of the case the most appropriate way of providing the care and medical treatment of which the patient stands in need" *(Section 13(2))*.

   The Act does not define "a suitable manner" but the Code of Practice offers some guidance (see above).

2. The wishes of the patient's relatives should be taken into account. In the case of an admission for assessment, the ASW is not bound either to consult relatives if this is not practicable nor to abide by their wishes. There is a duty to inform the nearest relative "before or within a reasonable time after" the ASW has made the application *(Section 11(3))*.

Before making an application for admission for treatment or for guardianship, the ASW must consult the patient's nearest relative (if any) unless this is not reasonably practicable or would involve unreasonable delay. The application cannot be made if the nearest relative objects.

Faced with such an objection, the ASW, if sufficient grounds exist, i.e. that it is unreasonable and against the interests of the patient, may apply for the patient's admission for assessment (Section 2) and initiate action in the County Court to displace the relative. The patient will remain liable to detention until the matter is finally decided.

3. The form of compulsory admission should be appropriate to the needs of the patient, must comply strictly with the law and should be "the least restrictive alternative". Section 4 should only be used in cases of genuine emergency or urgency. Section 2 may be used as a short-term treatment order.

4. The ASW should ensure that all the relevant documents are properly completed, e.g. that they are signed, conform to time limits, agree on names, etc. Statements made by others, e.g. in medical recommendations, may be taken at face value unless known to be false.

If, after proper consideration, an application is made, then:

1. The duly completed documents place the patient in the legal custody of the applicant who has "all the powers, authorities, protection and privileges which a constable has . . ." in respect of him *(Section 137(2)).*

The use of force should be avoided unless this is impossible. Help should be sought from colleagues, police, etc.

2. The applicant may authorise another person to take the patient to hospital *(Section 6(1)).* Such authority is best given in writing. The Section documents should accompany the patient.

58

3. The ASW should not act in the absence of any documents. Reliance must not be placed on promises that they await her arrival at hospital.

4. Health authorities have a duty to provide ambulance transport if needed to convey a detained patient to hospital.

5. The patient must be admitted to hospital within the time allowed (14 days from the date of the last medical examination for Sections 2 or 3, 24 hours from the date of the medical examination or the application, whichever is earlier, for Section 4).

6. The patient remains in the custody of the applicant until the documents are received by a person authorised by the hospital managers. On arrival at the hospital, the ASW should ensure that the person receiving the documents is so authorised.

7. If the patient absconds before admission, he can be retaken within 28 days (72 hours for Sections 4, 135 and 136) *(Section 138).*

Eleven
The Nearest Relative

The identification of the patient's nearest relative is explained in Sections 26 to 30 of the Act.

Some changes have been made from the 1959 Act, principally in giving equality to the patient's mother, priority to relatives caring for the patient and the status of relatives to those people with whom the patient has lived for five years or more. Thus the patient's Nearest Relative may not be next of kin for other purposes or the person who was Nearest Relative under the 1959 Act.

Usually, the nearest relative's identity is easily established but occasionally it may be less obvious.

The process is in two stages. Firstly, it is necessary to identify "relatives" within the meaning of the Act and to rank them in order of precedence. Secondly, the "nearest" of these relatives must be established.

"Relative" means:
- (a) husband or wife
- (b) son or daughter
- (c) father or mother
- (d) brother or sister
- (e) grandparent
- (f) grandchild
- (g) uncle or aunt
- (h) nephew or niece

Where two or more relatives have equal status:

(a) whole blood takes precedence over half blood, and

(b) the elder or eldest takes precedence.

Having established a hierarchy of relatives using the list above, certain of them may be *discounted:*

(a) relatives who have not attained the age of 18 years unless they are the husband, wife, father or mother of the patient;

(b) relatives resident outside the U.K., Channel Islands or Isle of Man if the patient ordinarily resides within that area;

(c) a permanently separated or deserted husband or wife;

(d) a person divested of authority over the patient under Section 38 of the Sexual Offences Act 1956.

Others may be *added* to the list of relatives:

(a) cohabitees of at least six months duration, provided that a married patient is also separated from a legal spouse, count as husband/wife;

(b) a person other than a relative with whom the patient has ordinarily resided for at least 5 years. Such a person follows (h) in the hierarchy.

Who is the "nearest relative"?

(a) The person who stands highest in the completed hierarchy above, unless

(b) another relative in the hierarchy takes precedence over (a) because the patient normally resides with or is cared for by him. *(Section 26(4))*

Note that thus the "5 years relative" usually becomes the "nearest relative".

In some circumstances the nearest relative may be the local authority, e.g. where parental rights have been assumed, where there is a Care Order or where a County Court has transferred the rights of the nearest relative to the authority.

Having identified the nearest relative, the social worker has no discretion to discount him or her, e.g. on grounds of age, disability, unsuitability, etc. It is possible for the nearest relative

61

to appoint another person to act for him or her *(Regulation 14)*. The ASW may also need to consider initiating action in the County Court to displace a nearest relative who has acted unreasonably and contrary to the patient's interests in refusing to agree to his admission for treatment or to guardianship or by discharging him. *(Section 29)*

Such action may also be desirable where the patient's illness is likely to be long term, he has no "nearest relative" and it is important for him to have an active and responsible person ready to protect his interests.

In such circumstances the patient's wishes are important but not paramount. The person appointed should be willing and able to act.

Rights and Powers of the Nearest Relative

1. To make application for the patient's admission under Part II of the Act. *(Section 11)*

    These rights and duties should be explained, preferably by an ASW who should explain why an application by the ASW may be preferable.

    The ASW should maintain contact with the nearest relative after the patient's admission and, where appropriate, keep him or her informed of the patient's progress. *(Code of Practice)*

2. To be informed by an ASW making application for admission for assessment "before or within a reasonable time after" such an application is made, and of his or her power to seek the patient's discharge under Section 23. *(Section 11(3))* The ASW is obliged to "have regard to" the relative's views. *(Section 13(1))*

    The duty of the ASW to inform the nearest relative is absolute and, unlike the hospital managers, she has no discretion not to do so at the patient's request. If conflict arises, the ASW should consult her superiors and, in exceptional circumstances, the Director of Social Services should be asked for advice as to the best way of informing the relative without distressing the patient.

3. To be *consulted* by an ASW before an application is made for admission for treatment or to guardianship, unless this is "not reasonably practicable or would involve unreasonable delay". If the nearest relative objects to the application, it cannot be made.

4. To refer the patient's case to the local social services authority so that an ASW may consider whether or not to make an application. If the ASW decides not to make such an application, she must inform the nearest relative of her reasons in writing. *(Section 13(4))*

   She should also discuss the case in detail with the nearest relative (preserving the confidentiality of the patient and records). She should tell the nearest relative of his or her right to make application.

5. If the patient is reclassified as suffering from a different form of mental disorder, the Responsible Medical Officer (RMO) must inform the nearest relative who may apply to the Mental Health Review Tribunal within 28 days. *(Section 16(4))*

6. To seek the discharge of a patient detained under Part 2, by giving 72 hours written notice to the hospital managers and subject to being barred by the RMO on grounds of danger. *(Sections 13 and 25)* The relative may apply to the Mental Health Review Tribunal within 28 days of being barred.

7. To seek the discharge of a patient under guardianship under Part 2, by giving notice to the local social services authority. There is no barring power and discharge becomes effective on receipt of the relative's notice. *(Section 23)*

63

8. Before exercising his or her power under 6 or 7 above, the nearest relative may authorise a doctor to examine the patient and give his advice. *(Section 24)*

9. To apply to the Mental Health Review Tribunal (q.v.) if barred from acting as nearest relative by a County Court. *(Section 29)*

10. To apply to the Mental Health Review Tribunal in respect of patients detained under Part III of the Act. (There is no equivalent to 6 above)

11. To make a complaint to the Mental Health Act Commission on behalf of a detained patient. *(Section 120)*

12. To be given information by the hospital managers as to the rights of detained patients and the protection afforded to them. *(Section 132(4))* The patient may request that such information is withheld from the nearest relative.

13. To be given, if practicable, seven days notice of a detained patient's impending discharge. The patient may request that this information be withheld. *(Section 133)*.

Twelve
Admission to Hospital or Guardianship

Most admissions to hospital or guardianship in which an Approved Social Worker (ASW) is concerned directly will be under powers conferred by Part II of the Act.

Crown Courts and Magistrates' Courts may commit patients appearing before them to hospital or guardianship under Part III. (See page 83)

Some patients may be admitted to hospital under Part X (Sections 135 and 136).

Informal Admission

Section 131 of the Act and Paragraphs 272 and 273 of the Memorandum make it clear that, for anyone over the age of 16 years and capable of expressing his own wishes, informal admission should be the norm "and should be used whenever a patient is not unwilling to be admitted, and can be treated without the use of compulsory powers". "No hospital should have a rule specifying times of day when only formal patients will be admitted".

The position of minors under the age of 16 or incapable of expressing their wishes is not made clear by the Act and parental consent is probably needed. (See Chapter 18)

The double negative in "not unwilling" is important. The patient does not have to request informal admission provided he does not object to it.

Therefore informal admission should be considered in all cases and compulsion used only where it is strictly necessary. Attempts by others to press for a hasty or avoidable use of compulsory powers should be resisted.

65

It should be noted that "admission" and "discharge" in the context of compulsory powers relate to the patient entering or leaving a state of detention in hospital, not to the hospital premises. An informal patient can be prevented from leaving hospital under Section 5 if necessary, and applications under Section 2 or 3 can be made where appropriate in respect of patients already in hospital.

The Code of Practice suggests a number of factors which may vitiate a patient's consent to an informal admission.

1. His failure to understand what is being proposed.

2. His inability, because of his mental condition, to understand or be able to express his views.

3. Sedation.

4. Vacillation or his inability to make a decision.

It may be necessary to try to establish the patient's true state of mind using clear evidence of his recent actions and expressed views as well as from his present behaviour.

Where the patient is willing to enter hospital informally, compulsion should only be used if:

1. his behaviour is so disturbed that he would be unmanageable without considerable physical restraint;

2. it is clear that he intends to refuse treatment which is clinically necessary;

3. he is making conditions which cannot be met;

4. although consenting now, his recent behaviour has been dangerous to himself or others and his state of mind may change so that he might leave hospital unless specially nursed.

The possible use of compulsion should never be used to induce consent to an informal admission. Indeed, compulsion should only be mentioned and explained after informal admission has been refused.

A patient should never be admitted informally where it has been pre-arranged that hospital staff will use Section 5 to detain him. Use of such powers should arise as and when necessary.

If conflict arises between doctors recommending compulsory admission and an ASW refusing to make an application, the doctors can obtain an application from the patient's nearest relative if willing. The ASW cannot prevent this. She may of course attempt to dissuade the relative. An opportunity to express her views may arise in the social circumstances report required by the hospital managers under Section 14.

Compulsory Admission

The following notes apply generally to Applications and Medical Recommendations. More detailed information may be found under the relevant Sections of the Act.

Applications

These may only be made by the nearest relative of the patient or by an Approved Social Worker who may act within or outside the area of her local authority.

It may be good practice for the ASW to make application as she has a duty to interview the patient, to consider all the circumstances of the case and possible alternative courses of action and to form a professional opinion based on special training. There are no such requirements laid upon the nearest relative. In law, he or she is not even required to have the patient's best interests at heart.

The applicant must personally have seen the patient within the previous 14 days for Sections 2, 3 and guardianship, or within the previous 24 hours for Section 4.

The application, except for Section 4, must be dated on or after the dates of the medical recommendations. In the case of Section 4, either the application or the medical recommendation may come first.

Applications for Admission by the Nearest Relative

The nearest relative is less well equipped to make application than the ASW and may find the situation difficult and stressful.

Doctors should not advise the nearest relative to make application in order to avoid involving an ASW because, e.g. the patient's condition is such that the ASW may not be able to interview him.

It may be proper for the doctor to advise the nearest relative to make application where the degree of urgency is such that admission is necessary before the ASW can arrive. In such circumstances, the doctor should remember that, as applicant, the relative will have the duty to remove the patient to hospital. Others may then need to seek directions from the relative, take over the removal and ensure that it is done sensitively.

Doctors should know and inform the nearest relative of his or her right to ask for an assessment by an ASW of the need to admit the patient. Doctors should also inform the nearest relative of his or her power to discharge the patient. They should also ensure that the relative is the *nearest* relative.

If an ASW is involved, she should not allow the nearest relative to make the application in order to avoid her own responsibilities. If the nearest relative has already made the application or strongly wishes to do so and the ASW agrees, she should give the relative all possible assistance.

Medical Recommendations

Two are required, except for Section 4. One must be given by a doctor approved under Section 12 as having "special experience in the diagnosis or treatment of mental disorder".

68

One should, if practicable, be given by a doctor having previous acquaintance with the patient.

Both of these conditions may be satisfied by the same doctor.

The doctors may examine the patient together and complete a joint form.

If the examinations are done separately, then not more than 5 days may elapse between them.

For Section 3 and guardianship, both medical recommendations must specify at least one form of mental disorder in common.

For Section 2, it is sufficient for the patient to meet the general definition of mental disorder contained in Section 1(2).

For Section 4, only one medical recommendation is necessary, preferably from a doctor with previous acquaintance with the patient. The doctor need not be approved.

Certain doctors are debarred from acting together to give medical recommendations. Briefly:

(a) Only one doctor may be on the staff of the hospital to which the patient is to be admitted. Neither may be on the staff of the mental nursing home to which the patient is to be admitted or of the hospital in the case of a private patient.

(b) A general practitioner employed part-time in a hospital does not count as being on its staff for (a).

(c) A doctor may not give a medical recommendation if he is the applicant, a partner of the applicant or of the other doctor, employed as an assistant by the applicant or other doctor, has any pecuniary interest in the patient, or is a relative of the patient, applicant or other doctor.

In the case of emergency or urgency where

(a) it is in the patient's best interest; *and*

69

(b) fulfilling the conditions of (a) above would cause delay involving serious risk to the health and safety of the patient; *and*

(c) one of the two doctors works at the hospital for less than half the time for which he is contracted to work for the NHS; *and*

(d) where one recommendation is made by a consultant, the other doctor does not work under him,

then both recommendations may be made by doctors on the staff of the hospital.

Admission for Assessment, Section 2
(or for assessment followed by medical treatment)

Application is made by the nearest relative on Form 1 or by an ASW on Form 2. The applicant must have seen the patient within the previous 14 days.

There must be two medical recommendations, as above, on Form 3 if joint or on Form 4 if separate. Admission must take place within 14 days of the date of the second medical examination.

The duration of the detention is for up to 28 days from the time of admission. It cannot be extended; Section 3 can be used subsequently, if necessary. A period of detention under Section 2 cannot be followed immediately and should not be followed closely by another. *(Memorandum, Paragraph 23)*

Discharge may be by the Responsible Medical Officer (RMO), hospital managers, Secretary of State, nearest relative (after giving 72 hours written notice and subject to bar by the RMO on the grounds of danger), or by the Mental Health Review Tribunal (q.v.).

The patient may apply to the Mental Health Review Tribunal within the first 14 days of detention.

70

Admission Criteria

(a) The presence of mental disorder (general definition).

(b) The disorder is of a nature or degree which warrants his detention for at least a limited period.

(c) The patient ought to be so detained in the interests of his own health or safety or for the protection of others.

Emergency Admission for Assessment, Section 4

N.B. *This should only be used in cases of genuine emergency or urgency where compliance with Section 2 would involve undesirable delay.*

The doctor must justify the use of this Section. It may be reasonable for the ASW to refuse to make an application if she is not satisfied that its use is justified or if she believes that the delay involved in obtaining the second medical recommendation will not cause risk to the patient or to others.

If the doctor and ASW disagree, it may be helpful for the opinion of a second ASW to be sought, though this is not binding on her colleague.

Whatever disagreement there may be, the patient and relatives should not be abandoned.

Application by the nearest relative is made on Form 5 or by the ASW on Form 6; the applicant must have seen the patient within the previous 24 hours.

One medical recommendation is required, preferably from a doctor who has previous acquaintance with the patient; this is made on Form 7.

Admission must take place within 24 hours from the time of the application or medical recommendation, whichever is earlier.

The duration of the detention is for up to 72 hours from admission. If a second medical recommendation complying

71

with Section 2 is received within this period, detention is converted to Section 2 and may continue for up to 28 days from admission.

Admission for Treatment, Section 3

The Code of Practice suggests that this Section is best used where the patient has recently been assessed and his needs are considered to be longer term or where he is already detained under Section 2.

Its use may cause unnecessary alarm to the patient and his relatives because of its duration. It may carry a stigma because it is associated with severe and intractable mental illness.

Application by the nearest relative is made on Form 8 or by the ASW on Form 9 after consultation with the nearest relative (unless this is impracticable).

Two medical recommendations from doctors are required on Form 10 if given jointly or on Form 11 if given separately. The same form(s) of mental disorder must be stated in the separate recommendations. Admission must take place within 14 days of the date of the later medical examination.

The duration of detention is for up to six months in the first instance renewable by the Responsible Medical Officer (RMO) for a further period of 6 months and then at yearly intervals. *(Section 20)*

The decision to discharge may be made by the RMO, the hospital managers, the Secretary of State, the nearest relative (subject to notice and possibility of bar by the RMO - see above as in Section 2 discharge), or the Mental Health Review Tribunal.

The patient may make one application to the Mental Health Review Tribunal at any time during each period of detention. The nearest relative may apply within 28 days of the request for discharge being barred by the RMO.

If no application is made, the hospital managers must refer the patient's case to the Mental Health Review Tribunal after 6 months and then after 3 years (after 1 year if the patient is under 16) if detention is renewed.

Admission Criteria

(a) The presence of one or more specific forms of mental disorder.

(b) The disorder is of a nature or degree which makes medical treatment in hospital appropriate.

(c) In the case of *psychopathic disorder or mental impairment,* "such treatment is likely to alleviate or prevent a deterioration of his condition".

(d) Such treatment is necessary for the health or safety of the patient or for the protection of others and it cannot be provided unless he is detained under this Section.

Renewal Criteria

(a), (b) and (d), as above; (c) now applies to all forms of mental disorder with an alternative in cases of *mental illness and severe mental impairment* that "the patient, if discharged, is unlikely to be able to care for himself, obtain the care he needs or guard himself against serious exploitation". *(Section 20(4))*

Leave of Absence

Patients subject to detention for assessment or treatment may be allowed leave of absence from the hospital, with or without conditions. *(Section 17)*

Anxiety has been expressed about patients being allowed extended leave from Section 3 on condition that they continue to take their medication under threat of being recalled to hospital if they do not do so, the so-called "long leash".

As good practice, the Mental Health Act Commission has made the following points:

73

1. Any use of Section 3 as a means of sending the patient immediately on conditional leave of absence in order that he have compulsory treatment in the community is wrong in law and practice.

2. Any use of Section 20 to nominally recall the patient from leave, to extend detention or to extend it without recall is wrong in law and practice.

3. If the patient's condition while on leave improves so that he can be discharged, this should be done. He should not be left on leave until the period of detention expires.

4. The power to grant leave with or without conditions is an essential means of assessing the patient's suitability for discharge. As part of this, a condition of treatment with the sanction of recall appears not to infringe any principle.

Detention of Patients Already in Hospital

If time allows, an informal patient already in hospital can be detained under Sections 2 or 3.

In urgent cases, the RMO or his nominated deputy may detain an in-patient whom he believes should be "admitted" for up to 72 hours under Section 5(2). This Section can be used by a non-psychiatrist in any hospital in respect of an in-patient who is not receiving treatment for mental disorder, but the patient must then be referred to a psychiatrist as soon as possible.

A nurse of the prescribed class (RMN or RNMH) may restrain an in-patient *who is already being treated for mental disorder* from leaving the hospital if this is immediately necessary in the interests of the patient's health or safety or for the protection of others and it is not practicable to secure the immediate attendance of a doctor empowered under Section 5(2). The nurse's holding power lasts for up to 6 hours, or the arrival of one of the two doctors empowered to act under Section 5(2). *(Section 5(4)*

74

Appeal to Hospital Managers for Discharge, Section 23

The first biennial Report of the Mental Health Act Commission states that, as hospital managers are primarily the people who "detain" the patient, they are liable at common law for any unjustified deprivation of his liberty. Thus they have a duty to end such deprivation as soon as it appears to be no longer justified.

A patient is entitled to ask the managers to discharge him at any time, and if he does so they must make a decision. This must be made by a committee or sub-committee of at least three managers and cannot be delegated to officers.

The amount of information required to enable the managers to reach a decision will vary from case to case. Formality should be avoided but they may need to consult the RMO, other professionals and the nearest relative and to interview the patient.

Such appeals should not be seen as a substitute for an application to the Mental Health Review Tribunal nor should they interfere with such an application.

There are similar provisions for patients subject to guardianship to appeal to the responsible social services authority.

Guardianship Orders

These may be made under Part II of the Act (Section 7) or Part III (Section 37). (q.v.) Considerable changes have been made in the powers of guardians by the 1983 Act. The guardian now has only three specific powers in respect of the patient.

1. To require the patient to reside at a specified place *(but not to convey him there)*.

2. To require the patient to attend at specified times and places for the purpose of medical treatment (but not to accept such treatment), education, training or occupation.

3. To require access to the patient to be given at the place where he is living to any doctor, ASW or other person specified by the guardian.

There is no equivalent to the general parental powers given by the 1959 Act.

Patients absent without leave under (1) above may be taken into custody within 28 days of leaving, and returned. After 28 days absence, guardianship lapses.

There are no other general powers of enforcement, though persons who induce or knowingly assist a patient to absent himself without leave, or harbour him or refuse to allow access to him may be committing an offence under Sections 128 or 129.

The guardian may be the local social services authority (who may in all cases refuse guardianship) or any suitable person who is willing to act and is acceptable to the local social services authority.

The criteria for admission to guardianship are basically the same as for Section 3 but the nature of the mental disorder must be sufficient to warrant guardianship "in the interests of the *welfare* of the patient or for the protection of other persons". *(Section 7(2)).*

The patient must have attained the age of 16 years.

Applications may be made by the nearest relative of the patient on Form 17 or by an ASW on Form 18, after consulting that relative.

Duration and renewal are as for Section 3. The nearest relative has the right of discharge (except when the order is made under Part III) and this cannot be barred. Application may also be made to the Mental Health Review Tribunal as for Section 3.

Guardianship was not commonly used under the 1959 Act, and the original Memorandum to the 1983 Act does not envisage its greater use. It suggests that, for minors, child care legislation may be used more appropriately.

The Code of Practice describes guardianship as enabling "the establishment of an authoritative framework for working with a patient with a minimum of constraint to achieve as independent a life as possible within the community". Therefore doctors and ASWs should always consider guardianship as a possible alternative to compulsory admission to hospital. It should only be rejected on evidence that assessment and treatment (including care) would be impossible without more restriction and compulsion.

It is suggested that guardianship should be used more frequently,

- as an immediate alternative to compulsory admission to hospital;

- to transfer detained patients from hospital where they show stable improvement but still need some degree of control;

- to provide supervised care and protection for informal patients who need more than usual help on discharge;

- to enable the elderly mentally disordered to live outside hospital;

- for young people leaving care;

- for young offenders under Part III of the Act;

- to provide structure and protection for brain-damaged patients.

Patients subject to guardianship may be admitted to hospital informally or for assessment. An admission for treatment cancels it. Guardianship should not be used to *require* a patient to reside in hospital. Nor should it be used to compel an unwilling person to enter residential accommodation.

77

If the guardian is the social services authority, an individual worker should be nominated to act for it. If the guardian is a private person, an ASW should be nominated to liaise with him or her.

Two social workers should be responsible for explaining to the patient the reasons for and implications of guardianship and his rights to discharge and to apply to the Mental Health Review Tribunal. This should be recorded in the case file.

The success of guardianship depends upon a number of factors:

1. A competent and willing guardian.

2. Professional support and advice for the guardian as necessary.

3. An acceptable place of residence for the patient which facilitates care and treatment and ensures the protection of others.

4. Facilities for day care, education, training and occupation accessible to the patient.

5. Mutually co-operative relationships between the patient, ASW, doctor, CPN, guardian and others involved.

6. Endorsement of the arrangement by all concerned with the welfare of the patient and the support of the patient's family.

7. The patient's condition being such that care in the community is the most appropriate arrangement.

Entry to Hospital under Part X

Section 135 allows forced access to a patient.

ASWs have powers of entry under Section 115 (see page 46). Refusal to allow this may be an offence *(Section 129)* but normally entry cannot be forced.

Procedure

An ASW lays information on oath before a Justice of the Peace that "there is reasonable cause to suspect that a person believed to be suffering from mental disorder :-

(a) has been, or is being, ill-treated, neglected or kept otherwise than under control . . . or

(b) being unable to care for himself, is living alone . . ."

The Justice may issue a warrant authorising any police constable (who need not be named) to enter the premises, if need be by force, and if thought fit remove the patient to a Place of Safety with a view to the making of an application under Part II or other arrangements in respect of him. *(Section 135(1)).*

The patient need not be named. *(Section 135(5))*

In executing the warrant, the constable must be accompanied by an ASW and a doctor who can make whatever arrangements are necessary.

"Place of Safety" includes Part III Accommodation, any hospital or mental nursing home, residential accommodation for mentally disordered persons, a police station or any other suitable place the occupier of which is willing to receive the patient temporarily. *(Section 135(6))*

The patient may be detained there for up to 72 hours. However, if a police station is used, the patient should remain there for the shortest time practicable while other arrangements are made.

Once the patient has been removed to a Place of Safety, the warrant is exhausted. If the patient is moved to another place, this must be done under other appropriate powers.

Any period of detention under Section 135 is additional to subsequent periods under Part II.

If the patient is found not to be mentally disordered, or not to require removal to a Place of Safety, the ASW and doctor have no further authority to remain on his premises if requested to leave.

Similar powers exist under Section 135(2) in respect of patients absent without leave. The information may be laid by any constable or other person authorised to take or retake the patient. In executing the warrant, the constable *may* be accompanied by an ASW and/or doctor or by any person authorised to retake the patient.

Section 48 of the National Assistance Act 1948 places a duty on the local authority to safeguard the property of a person admitted to hospital where it is aware of the circumstances, e.g. by being involved in the admission, and it appears that there is a danger of loss or damage to any movable property and no other suitable arrangements have been or are being made. The authority has powers to enter and do whatever is necessary to secure the premises and property.

Section 136 authorises a police constable who finds in a public place "a person who appears to him to be suffering from mental disorder and to be in immediate need of care or control . . . if he thinks it necessary to do so in the interests of the person or for the protection of other persons" to remove him to a Place of Safety.

The patient may be detained there for up to 72 hours to enable him to be medically examined and interviewed by an ASW so that appropriate arrangements can be made. It is unlikely that Section 4 could be justified.

A police station should be used for the shortest possible time. Patients in police custody have rights (e.g. to legal advice) under the Police and Criminal Evidence Act.

Thirteen
Admission through the Courts.

Part III of the Act deals with the powers of the criminal courts and the Home Secretary to admit to hospital or guardianship persons charged before the courts with offences or convicted of them.

Three new powers came into effect on 1st October 1984.

1. **Remand to hospital for reports** which may be used where it is more appropriate than remands in custody or on bail. *(Section 35)*

   The power may be exercised by a Crown Court in respect of any person awaiting trial or at any stage of a trial for an offence punishable by imprisonment, other than a person convicted of murder.

   A Magistrates' Court may exercise the power in respect of any person convicted of an offence punishable by that court with imprisonment or any person charged with such an offence if the court is satisfied as to his guilt or he has consented to the remand.

   In either case the court must be satisfied on the written or oral evidence of an approved doctor that the patient is suffering from one of the four specific forms of mental disorder, that a bed is or will be available within 7 days and that it would be impracticable to obtain the reports if he were remanded on bail.

   Remand is for 28 days in the first instance, renewable if necessary to complete the reports to a maximum period of 12 weeks.

   The patient may commission an independent medical report at his own expense and use it as the basis for the remand to be terminated.

81

2. **Remand to hospital for treatment.** *(Section 36).*

This power may be exercised by the Crown Court in respect of any person awaiting trial or at any stage of such a trial prior to sentence for an offence, other than murder, punishable with imprisonment.

The court must be satisfied on the written or oral evidence of two doctors, one of whom must be approved, that the patient is suffering from mental illness or severe mental impairment of a nature or degree which makes detention in hospital for treatment appropriate. A bed must be available within 7 days.

Remand is for 28 days, and can be extended to a maximum of 12 weeks if warranted.

The patient may seek to have the remand terminated through an independent medical report obtained at his own expense.

3. **An Interim Hospital Order** may be made by the Crown Court or Magistrates' Court in respect of an offender convicted of an offence, other than murder, punishable with imprisonment. *(Section 38)*

The intention is for this power to give a trial period to assess the patient's suitability for a full Hospital Order without the need to make an irrevocable decision.

The power may be exercised if the court is satisfied, on the written or oral evidence of two doctors, one of whom must be approved, that the patient is suffering from one of the four specific forms of mental disorder and that this is such that a Hospital Order may be appropriate. A bed must be available within 28 days.

In the first instance, the order lasts for 12 weeks, renewable for up to 6 months.

Hospital and Guardianship Orders   *(Section 37)*

These may be made by the Crown Court or the Magistrates' Court in respect of a person convicted of an offence, other than murder, punishable with imprisonment. A Magistrates' Court may exercise the power of making a Hospital Order in respect of an unconvicted person suffering from *mental illness or severe mental impairment* if it is satisfied as to his guilt.

The power to make a Hospital Order can only be exercised if:

1. The court is satisfied on the evidence of two doctors, one of whom must be approved, that the patient is suffering from one of the four specific forms of mental disorder of a nature or degree which warrants detention in hospital for treatment.

2. In the case of psychopathic disorder and mental impairment, that treatment is likely to alleviate or prevent a deterioration in his condition.

3. A bed is or will be available within 28 days.

4. Both doctors describe the patient as suffering from the same form of disorder.

5. Having regard to all the circumstances and possible alternatives, the court is satisfied that a Hospital Order is the most appropriate action.

For Guardianship Orders, the court must be satisfied as to (1) above but the nature or degree of disorder must warrant guardianship. The patient must have reached the age of 16 years.

The effect is similar to an admission for treatment or to guardianship made under Part II except that the nearest relative has no right to consultation or of discharge. The requirements as to medical recommendations are broadly similar to Part II but the court takes on the role of the applicant. It is renewable as for Section 3.

83

A Hospital Order can only be made if a hospital is willing to admit the patient and guardianship can be rejected by the local social services authority.

The patient or his nearest relative may apply to the Mental Health Review Tribunal after the first 6 months as under Section 3.

Note: A patient may be admitted to hospital as a condition of bail or of a Probation Order. However, under mental health legislation such patients have informal status. If they attempt to leave the hospital they can only be prevented from doing so under Part II powers if these are appropriate and justified.

Restriction Orders *(Section 41)*

These may be made by the Crown Court at the same time as a Hospital Order. Magistrates' Courts do not possess this power but may remit an offender to Crown Court.

In addition to the requirements for a Hospital Order, the court must be satisfied that a Restriction Order should be made to protect the public from serious harm, having regard to the nature of the offence, the antecedents of the offender and the risk of him committing further offences if discharged.

The order may be made for a finite period or without limit of time.

The majority of restricted patients will be admitted to Special Hospitals.

The effect of a Restriction Order is that the patient may not leave hospital without the consent of the Home Secretary. The Hospital Order lasts, without the need for renewal, for the period of the Restriction Order.

Restriction Orders may be lifted by the Home Secretary and restricted patients may apply to the Mental Health Review Tribunal.

Transfer of Prisoners to Hospital

The Home Secretary has power to transfer remand or convicted prisoners from penal institutions to mental hospital for treatment.

He must be satisfied that the conditions for a Hospital Order exist and that, having regard to the public interest and all the circumstances, such a transfer is expedient. *(Sections 47 and 48)*

The patient is admitted to hospital under a Transfer Direction which has the same effect as a Hospital Order.

Restriction Directions

In the case of sentenced prisoners, the Home Secretary may also impose a Restriction Direction, in addition to the Transfer Direction.

This has the same effect as a Restriction Order but lasts only until the date on which the original sentence of imprisonment would have ended, taking into account any remission earned up to the date of transfer. *(Sections 49 to 51)*

Note: On the expiry of a Restriction Order or Restriction Direction, the patient is not automatically eligible for discharge from hospital. He is treated as if subject to a new Hospital Order made on the day his restriction ends.

Criminal Procedure (Insanity) Act 1964
Criminal Procedure (Insanity and Unfitness to Plead) Act 1991

Patients who are found unfit to plead or not guilty by reason of insanity are dealt with under these Acts.

The 1964 Act requires the court to make an order admitting the patient to a hospital specified by the Home Secretary as if subject to a Hospital Order with a Restriction Order without limit of time.

The 1991 Act gives the court alternatives such as making a Guardianship Order, a Supervision and Treatment Order or an absolute discharge. The second of these places the patient under the supervision of a social worker or probation officer and requires him to undergo medical treatment. It may also include a requirement as to residence.

At the time of writing, this Act has not yet been implemented and will come into force on a date to be specified by the Secretary of State.

Fourteen

Consent to Treatment

Part IV of the Mental Health Act 1983 limits the power of doctors, except in an emergency, to give certain treatments to patients. For some irreversible treatments the patient must give real consent which must be validated independently. These safeguards apply to all patients *(Section 57)*. Some other treatments may only be given to patients who consent, or whose lack of consent is overridden by an independent second opinion. These safeguards apply only to longer term detained patients *(Section 58)*.

"Real consent" must be genuine, uninfluenced by coercion or by fraud or misdescription, and must be based on sufficient information. The Code of practice describes consent as:

> *...the voluntary and continuing permission of the patient to receive a particular treatment based on an adequate knowledge of the purpose, nature, likely effects and risks of that treatment, including the likelihood of its success and any alternatives to it... Permission given under any unfair pressure is not 'consent'.*

Social workers, not necessarily ASWs, may be involved in consultation under this part of the Act as professionals concerned with the patient's treatment.

It is important therefore that social workers have sufficient knowledge of treatments to be able to take an informed part in such consultations. It is usually easy to identify a nurse who has been involved in treatment, but it may be more difficult to identify a second professional who has. Thus social workers may find themselves cast in this role.

The first biennial Report of the Mental Health Act Commission says that, in a series of 213 visits made for this purpose, 82% of the second professionals consulted were social workers.

The treatments, safeguards and procedures fall into two groups which may be specified in the Act itself or added by Regulations or by the Code of Practice.

Section 57, "Consent *and* Second Opinion"

This covers certain irreversible treatments and extends to all patients. These treatments are:

(a) psychosurgery, i.e. a surgical operation aimed at destroying brain tissue;

(b) the *implantation* of hormones into a patient to reduce male sexual drive.

The doctor must explain the treatment fully to the patient and obtain his real consent.

The Commission will send three people to the hospital. One will be a doctor approved by the Commission for the purpose of considering second opinions; the others will be non-medical members.

Together, the three persons must interview the patient and certify that he has given his real consent.

The medically qualified member will examine the patient, discuss his case with the doctor wishing to give the treatment and certify that it is appropriate. He must also, before agreeing, consult two other persons professionally concerned with the patient's treatment. One of these must be a nurse, the other neither a nurse nor a doctor.

Even after this consultation and validation procedure has been done, the patient may withdraw his consent, in which case the treatment cannot be given.

Section 58, "Consent *or* Second Opinion"

This relates to certain less serious treatments and covers only longer term compulsorily detained patients, i.e. those under Sections 2 or 3 or Part III orders which have similar effects to Section 3.

These treatments are:

(a) ECT;

(b) drug treatment given by any means after a period of 3 months during any continuous period of detention, including the situation where one period of detention, e.g. under Section 2, is followed immediately by a further period, e.g. under Section 3.

If the patient is able to give real consent, then the treatment may be given.

If real consent cannot be obtained, the Commission must be contacted for a second medical opinion. In the case of ECT or of urgency, this should be forthcoming within two working days.

The Commission will send the Second Opinion Appointed Doctor (S.O.A.D.) who will consult with the patient's RMO and with two other professionals as above and, if satisfied, approve the treatment or a plan of treatment. The treatment may then be given, even though the patient has not consented to it.

For treatment under both Sections, the Commission will require reports from the patient's doctor and may order that the treatment is discontinued.

Urgent treatment may be given in certain situations without the safeguards described above, pending a second opinion. *(Section 62).*

These are:

(a) any treatment which is immediately necessary to save the patient's life. Treatments for mental disorder will rarely fall into this category;

(b) a treatment which is not irreversible and is immediately necessary to prevent a serious deterioration in the patient's condition;

(c) a treatment which is not irreversible or hazardous and is immediately necessary to alleviate serious suffering;

(d) a treatment which is not irreversible or hazardous, is immediately necessary and represents the minimum interference necessary to prevent the patient from behaving violently or being a danger to himself or to others.

Fifteen

Mental Health Review Tribunals

Mental Health Review Tribunals (MHRT) were established under the Mental Health Act 1959. Their composition remains unchanged in the 1983 Act, though their powers have been increased, as have the number of opportunities available to patients to apply to them. If patients do not make application, hospital managers now have a duty to refer their cases to Tribunals. Legal aid is now available to patients.

There is a separate MHRT for each English Regional Health Authority and one for the whole of Wales. They operate through four offices.

Composition is explained in Schedule 2 of the Act. Briefly, members are appointed by the Lord Chancellor and fall into medical, legal and lay groups. The Chairman of each Tribunal and the President of each panel are appointed from the legally qualified group.

The chart on the next page explains how applications are made to the MHRT in respect of **Part II patients.**

Part III Patients

(a) Guardianship - as for Part II (see chart)

(b) Hospital Orders (with or without a Restriction Order). These patients have similar rights of application as Section 3 patients except that, in general, they cannot apply within the first six months period of detention. Similarly, their case must be referred to a Tribunal after 3 years if no application has been made.

Since the nearest relative has no right of discharge under Part III, he or she has the right to apply to the MHRT within the time periods allowed to the patient.

91

Applications to MHRT - Part II Patients

*Only **one** application may be made in each period*

Section	Patient may apply	Nearest Relative may apply	Hospital Managers must refer to MHRT
Section 2	within first 14 days of detention		
Section 3	at any time in first 6 months		After 6 months if no application made. Thereafter, if detention renewed, after 3 years without Tribunal (1 year if under 16)
Renewed	at any time in period for which detention renewed		
Guardianship	at any time in first 6 months		
Renewed	at any time in period for which renewed		
Reclassified (Section 16)	within first 28 days of being informed	within first 28 days of being informed	
Transferred to hospital from guardianship	within first 6 months of detention in hospital		
RMO bars relative's discharge (Section 25)		within first 28 days of being informed	
Nearest relative displaced by County Court (Section 29)		in first 12 months of Order, then once in each subsequent period of 12 months for which Order remains in force	

92

(For full information and exceptions to (b) above, see the Memorandum, Paragraph 217 et seq.)

How to apply

Application is made in writing to the appropriate office giving details of the patient's name, address, hospital or responsible local social services authority, the Section under which the patient is detained, the nearest relative and legal representative. The statutory form may be used but is not essential.

The patient need not inform the hospital; however, if he seeks help in applying, this should be given.

Procedure

On receipt of an application, the MHRT must notify the patient if he is not the applicant, the hospital or local social services authority and the Home Secretary in the case of restricted patients.

The hospital or local social services authority must submit reports on the patient's case history and background information and up-to-date medical and social reports, to include the writer's view as to the suitability of the patient for discharge.

The contents, or part of them, may be withheld from the patient if "disclosure would adversely affect his health or welfare" but they must be disclosed in full to his legal representative.

For Section 2 patients, the Tribunal must hear the case within 7 days.

As legal aid is now available, social workers may wish to help the patient apply for this.

The Hearing

Hearings are usually held at the hospital in which the patient is detained or, for guardianship cases, in suitable local authority premises.

Hearings are usually in private. The patient may request a public hearing but this can be refused. If so, the reason must be recorded. There is no reporting.

Usually there will be three Tribunal members, one from each group, with the legal member presiding. There is provision for this to be a High Court Judge if appropriate.

The Tribunal may conduct its business as it wishes, e.g. under subpoena, on oath or informally (which is the most usual). The President will explain the procedure and should seek to avoid undue formality.

The rules of natural justice must be followed.

Any person, including the patient, may be excluded and any person may be heard.

The medical member must examine the patient, in private if appropriate, and have access to his case records. His report is confidential to the Tribunal.

Any other member may interview the patient, in private if appropriate, and must do so if requested by the patient.

The Social Work Role

1. The Tribunal will require an up-to-date social report on the patient within 3 to 6 weeks of the application (a shorter period for Section 2 cases). This should include

   (a) home and family circumstances, including attitude of the nearest relative;

   (b) opportunities for housing, occupation or employment on discharge;

   (c) community support and medical facilities available;

   (d) financial circumstances.

The social worker will probably be required to attend the Tribunal.

2. A social worker who has been involved with the patient and/or his family, or who has supervised the patient while on leave or who will supervise him if discharged may be asked to attend.

3. An independent social report may be commissioned by the patient or his legal representative.

It should be remembered that the primary function of the Tribunal is not to look at the patient's condition on admission, at the application or the circumstances of it. Rather it considers his current situation.

Tribunal Powers (Part II Patients)

1. Section 2 patients *must* be discharged if not suffering from mental disorder of a nature or degree which warrants his detention or if such detention is not necessary in the interests of the patient's health or safety or for the protection of others.

2. Section 3 patients *must* be discharged if not suffering from one of the specific forms of mental disorder of a nature or degree to warrant detention or if detention is not warranted in the interests of the patient's health or safety or for the protection of others.

3. Section 25 patients (where the nearest relative's power to discharge has been barred) *must* be discharged if the patient, if released, would not be likely to act in a manner dangerous to others or himself.

4. Guardianship patients *must* be discharged if not suffering from one of the four specific forms of mental disorder or where guardianship is not necessary in the interests of the welfare of the patient or for the protection of others.

5. The Tribunal *may* discharge unrestricted patients (except for Section 2) where there is little likelihood of medical treatment alleviating or preventing a deterioration of the patient's condition and, in the case of mental illness or severe mental impairment, the patient, if discharged, is likely to be able to care for himself or obtain the care he needs to guard himself against serious exploitation.

6. In addition to its powers of discharge, the Tribunal *may* recommend leave of absence, delayed discharge or transfer to another hospital. It may reconvene if its recommendations are not complied with.

Note: *"discharge"* is from *detention* in hospital; the patient may remain there informally.

Part III Unrestricted Patients

The Tribunal's powers are the same as for Part II patients.

Part III Restricted Patients

1. The Tribunal *must* order the *absolute discharge* of a patient under a Restriction Order if the conditions of (2) above are met and he need not remain liable to recall to hospital.

2. It *must* order his *conditional discharge* if (2) above is satisfied but recall powers should be retained. It may defer its decision until proper arrangements have been made and approved. After 12 months, and subsequently at intervals of 2 years, such patients may apply to the Tribunal for an absolute discharge. If the patient is recalled to hospital, the Home Secretary must refer the case to the Tribunal within one month.

3. There is no equivalent of (5) above in the case of restricted patients; they are not entitled automatically to discharge if they are not deriving benefit from treatment.

4. Patients subject to Restriction Directions are liable to be returned to prison pending trial or to resume their sentence if they no longer require treatment in hospital. Therefore the Tribunal cannot discharge them absolutely or conditionally in the normal way. If it finds that the patient's condition would otherwise allow him to be discharged, it may recommend that he remain in hospital rather than being returned to prison. In the case of a remand prisoner, the Home Secretary must return him to prison unless such a recommendation is made. For sentenced prisoners, the Home Secretary may allow discharge. A decision must be made within 90 days.

5. The Tribunal may also recommend alternatives as under (6) above, but their implementation is at the discretion of the Home Secretary.

Sixteen

Some Functions of the Local Authority

Part VIII of the Act

1. Section 114 places a duty on a local social services authority to appoint a sufficient number of ASWs to carry out its duties under the Act. Attention must be given to such directions as the Secretary of State may issue and ASWs must have "appropriate competence".

2. Section 116 restates the duty of local authorities to arrange visits to certain patients in any hospital and take such steps in regard to them as would be expected of a parent. Such patients are:

    (a) children and young persons over whom parental rights have been assumed under child care legislation;

    (b) a person subject to the local authority's guardianship;

    (c) a person in respect of whom the functions of nearest relative have been transferred to the local authority.

3. Section 117 reinforces the duty of local social services authorities together with district health authorities in co-operation with voluntary agencies to provide appropriate aftercare for as long as it is needed for patients who are:

    (a) discharged from detention under Section 3;

    (b) discharged from detention under a Transfer Direction (Sections 47 or 48);

    (c) discharged from a Hospital Order (Section 37).

It is good practice for the RMO and other members of the discharge planning team to monitor the patient's progress after discharge. A key worker - a community psychiatric nurse or social worker - may liaise with the hospital team until the patient is sufficiently settled for the social services department to take full responsibility.

Where aftercare is to be provided by the Probation Service (usually ex-restricted patients) the probation officer should be involved in the pre-discharge planning and post-discharge review.

District health authorities and social services departments should provide a full range of services, with close liaison, clear fixing of responsibilities and provision of funds to meet them.

Volunteers may be helpful, especially in mental handicap training programmes. They should attend case conferences and share in decisions.

There may be special problems in the aftercare of patients from minority ethnic groups who may require special measures.

Seventeen

The Mental Health Act Commission

This multi-disciplinary body is established as a special health authority responsible to the Secretary of State. It operates from three regional offices and has a central policy committee.

Among its duties are:

(a) the preparation of a Code of Practice and biennial reports;

(b) the operation of Part IV of the Act (Consent to Treatment);

(c) the review of a decision to withhold a postal packet if an application is made for it to do so (Section 121(7));

(d) the general protection of detained patients and the investigation of unresolved complaints made by them or on their behalf;

(e) any other matter directed by the Secretary of State.

The Commission's functions are completely separate from those of Mental Health Review Tribunals and it has no power of discharge.

Eighteen

Children and Young People under the age of 18

There are special difficulties in respect of mentally disordered people who are under the age of 16 or under 18 and not capable of expressing their own wishes.

In general there is no minimum age limit for admission to hospital. Young people aged between 16 and 18 who are capable of expressing their own wishes are dealt with as adults. Wards of Court can only be admitted to hospital, guardianship, etc. with the consent of the Judge.

The Code of Practice contains guidance that young people should be kept fully informed and their views taken into account. They should have the right to make their own decisions, especially about treatment, if they are capable of doing so and not overruled by statute law. Any intervention into their lives because of mental disorder should be the least restrictive possible and minimise segregation from their family, friends, etc.

When considering care and treatment, it should be established who is legally responsible for decisions about the child; who has custody; how mature and capable is the child; if parents refuse consent, is this reasonable; is treatment necessary and viable.

In general, parents or guardians may arrange the informal admission of children under 16. However, where such children are deemed capable of making such decisions for themselves, this parental power lapses and there is no authority to detain the child.

Consent to Treatment

A child under 16 may be capable of deciding for him/herself. If not, parental consent will suffice. If this is withheld, consideration may need to be given to child care legislation or wardship

Young people aged 16 to 18 can make their own decisions unless deemed incapable, in which case consent can be given by the parent or guardian. It should not be assumed that parental agreement to admission also gives permission for treatment.

Secure Accommodation

The Child Care Act 1980 (Section 21A) requires that, where a child in care is placed in a National Health Service secure unit or private nursing home and this restriction of liberty is to last longer than 72 hours, application must be made to a juvenile court. This does not apply to those detained under the Mental Health Act.

Nineteen

Medication

It is difficult to give complete, current and accurate information about the drugs used in the treatment of mental disorder. There are so many available, with new drugs being introduced constantly, that any list soon becomes outdated.

Individual doctors may have their own favourite remedies. Individual patients may vary in their response to apparently similar preparations.

Different manufacturers may produce identical or very similar drugs but market them under different brand names in different tablet colours, shapes, sizes, etc. This confusion is compounded as each drug has at least two names, an "official" name and a "proprietary" name. Patients obtaining medication from a hospital will be given "official" drugs which may look quite different from the identical substance supplied under its "proprietary" name by a general practitioner. The situation should be improved by the limited list now available.

In addition to their desired therapeutic effects, drugs may produce unwanted side-effects. These tend to vary in incidence and severity according to the dosage, the duration of treatment and the individual patient's response. Sometimes they may become more severe if the drug is continued; in other cases they may become less troublesome as treatment proceeds.

Social workers who are in regular contact with clients who are taking medication should not ignore this fact as being outside their professional brief. The effects or side-effects of the drug may alter the client's capacity to concentrate, his co-ordination, his physical and mental processes, etc. It may be the social worker who first becomes, or is made aware of the advent of side-effects. If these are reported quickly to the doctor, the client may be spared much discomfort and anxiety, and may be enabled to continue with necessary treatment, perhaps with an alteration of dosage or change of drug.

In the list which follows, drugs have been grouped firstly into the type of mental disorder for which they are commonly used. Secondly, similar drugs have been placed together. Only a few common examples of each type of drug are given.

Neurosis, Anxiety, etc

Proprietary Name	Official Name	Usual Dose	Side-Effects	Special Notes
Librium	Chlordiazepoxide	10mgm 3 times daily	All these drugs can cause reduced blood pressure and drowsiness	All of these drugs reduce the patient's tolerance for alcohol.
Melleril	Thioridazine HCl	30-100 mgm daily. May be increased		The ability to drive, operate machinery, may be reduced.
Serenid-D	Oxazepam	15-30mgm 3 times daily		Possibility of dependence on and tolerance to these drugs.
Valium	Diazepam	6-40mgm daily		Possibility of convulsions when high doses are stopped suddenly
Mogadon	Nitrazepam	5-10mgm before retiring		Used for insomnia associated with anxiety.

Depression

Proprietary Name	Official Name	Usual Dose	Side-Effects	Special Notes
Allegron	Nortriptyline HCl	25mgm 3-4 times daily	With all of these drugs -	
Aventyl	Nortriptyline	25mgm 3-4 times daily	blurred vision dry mouth constipation	All of these drugs may potentiate the action of other drugs
Concordin	Protriptyline HCl	15-60mgm daily in divided doses	retention of urine	and of alcohol. Use with caution with MAOIs
Lenzitol	Amitriptyline HCl (sustained release)	25-50mgm daily		Use lower dose in the elderly
Tryptizol	Amitriptyline HCl	25mgm 3 times daily. May be increased to 150mgm daily		
Anafranil	Clomipramine HCl	50-75mgm daily in divided doses		
Pertofran	Desipramine HCl	50-75mgm daily at first, may increase later		
Sinequan	Doxepin HCl	0-300 mgm daily in divided doses		
Surmontil	Trimipramine	50-100 mgm before retiring		
Tofranil	Imipramine HCl	50-150 mgm daily		

Depression (cont)

Proprietary Name	Official Name	Usual Dose	Side-Effects	Special Notes
Optimax	L-tryptophan	Tablets: 4-12 daily. Powder: 20-60mgm daily	Drowsiness Feeling of fullness Nausea at first	The powder is mixed with chocolate and makes a palatable drink. It is particularly useful in the elderly.
Marplan	Isocarboxazid	**Mono-Amine Oxidose Inhibitors (MAOI)** All drugs of this type require that the patient avoids certain foods, e.g. bananas pickled herrings meat extracts (Oxo, Bovril, etc.) yeast extracts (Marmite, etc.) broad beans cheese alcoholic beverages yoghurt game meat They also potentiate many other drugs. Failure to observe these precautions may cause severe side-effects which can be fatal - raised blood pressure, headache, possible stroke.		
Nardil	Phenelzine			
Niamid	Nialamide			
Parnate	Tranylcypromine			
Camcolit	Lithium Carbonate		Unsteady gait Nausea or vomiting Drowsiness Abdominal pain Thirst Dry mouth Tremor	Treatment should begin in hospital under careful controls. If side-effects occur, treatment should be stopped for several days and restarted on lower dose.
Priadel	Lithium Carbonate (sustained release)			These preparations are used to reduce the frequency of attack in Manic Depressive psychosis.

106

Mania

Proprietary Name	Official Name	Usual Dose	Side-Effects	Special Notes
Largactil	Chlorpromazine	25mgm or more 3 times daily	All drugs of this type may cause:-	
Serenace	Haloperidol	0.5mgm twice daily	Drowsiness Reduced blood pressure	Serenace is said to cause less liver damage
Triperidol	Trifluperidol	0.5 - 2.5 mgm daily	Weight gain Liver damage Bone marrow damage Hypersensitivity to sun light (UVL) Parkinsonism-like symptoms	
Camcolit	See under "Depression"			
Priadel				

Schizophrenia

Fentazin	Perphenazine	12mgm daily in divided doses	All drugs of this type may cause:- Drowsiness	To avoid or reduce Parlinsonism-like symptoms, drugs such as *Artane, Congentin, Disipal,* etc. may be administered concurrently
Largactil	Chlorpromazine HCl	25mgm or more 3 times daily	Low blood pressure Weight gain	
Modecate	Fluophenazine decanoate	25mgm every 15 - 35 days	Liver damage Bone marrow damage	Intra-muscular injection
Moditen	Fluophenazine enanthate	25mgm every 15 - 35 days	Hypersensitivity to sunlight (UVL)	Intra-muscular injection
Serenace	Haloperidol	0.5mgm twice daily	Parkinsonism-like symptoms	
Stelazine	Trifluoperazine	10mgm or more daily	Skin rashes	

Senile Dementia - Alzheimer's Disease

Proprietary Name	Official Name	Usual Dose	Side-Effects	Special Notes
Hydergine	Co-Dergocrine Mersylate	1.5mgm 3 times daily or 4.5mgm once daily	Nausea, vomiting, flushes, rashes,nasal congestion, postural hypotension	May cause severe slowing of heart beat
Cyclobral Cyclospasmol	Cyclandelate	1.2-1.6g daily in divided doses	Nausea, flushing, dizziness in high doses	Contra-indicated following recent myocardial infarction
Defencin Duuadilan	Isoxsuprine HCl	20mgm 4 times daily	Flushing, nausea, vomiting, palpitations, raised heart rate	Contra-indicated after recent arterial haemorrhage
Praxilene	Naftidrofuryl Oxalate	100mgm 3 times daily	Nausea, epi- gastric pain	

108

STEP-BY-STEP THROUGH THE MENTAL HEALTH ACT, 1983

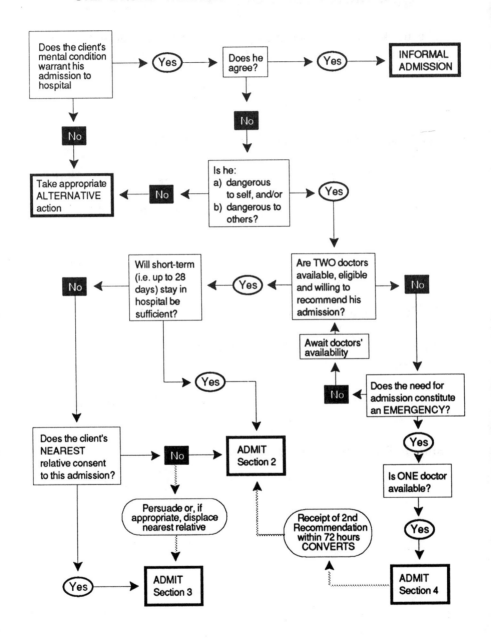

109

Suggestions for Further Reading

The books listed below may help to give the reader further information or alternative models of mental illness.

Sanity, Madness and the Family , by R D Laing & A Esterson, Pelican 1970.

The Divided Self , by R D Laing, Pelican 1970.

The Myth of Mental Illness, by T S Szasz, Harper and Row 1961.

Psychiatry for Students, by D Stafford-Clark, Allen and Unwin 1983.

The Causes and Cures of Neuroses, by H J Eysenck & S Rachman, Routledge and Kegan Paul 1965.

Psychiatry of Mental Handicap, by A H Reid, Blackwell 1982.

Coping with Loss, by R V Lascelles, (Second Edition), PEPAR 1991.

Managing Anxiety, by June Wen, (Second Edition), PEPAR 1992.

Suicide Prevention, by P J Vaughan, PEPAR 1985.

Subject Index

Absence
- leave of, 73
- without leave, 46, 59, 80
Absolute discharge, 86, 96
Admission
- emergency, 71
- for assessment, 70
- for treatment, 72
- informal, 65
- of in-patient, 74
- Section 135, 78
- Section 136, 80
- through Courts, 81-86
- to Guardianship, 75
Affective psychosis, 22
Aftercare, 98-99
Aggressive psychopath, 43
AIDS Dementia, 19
Alzheimer's disease, 20
Alzheimer-type brain failure, 19
Ambulance transport, 56, 59
Anxiety state, 12
Appeal
- to managers, 75
- to MHRT, 91-94
Applications
- for admission, 67
- by ASW, 44, 57-59
- by nearest relative, 68
Approved Social Worker, 44-59
- and doctors, 54-55
- and interviews, 50-51
- and nearest relative, 53-54
- and referrals, 49-50
- protection for, 47
- role in admissions, 57-59

Bail, hospital as condition of, 84
Brain failure, 19-21

Catatonic schizophrenia, 32
Children & Young Persons , 101-102
Commission, Mental Health Act, 100
Complaints, 100
Compulsory admission, 67
Conditional discharge, 96
Consent to treatment, 87-90

Consultation with relatives, 44, 53, 57, 63, 72
County Court, 45, 58, 61, 62
Creative psychopath, 43
Creuzfeld-Jakob Syndrome, 19
Criminal Procedure (Insanity) Acts, 85
Crown Court, 81 et seq

Delusions
- grandiose, 27
- nihilistic, 23
- schizophrenic, 31
Dementia, 19-21
Depression
- endogenous, 22-25
- manic, 22
- reactive, 14-16
Discharge
- absolute, 86, 96
- by managers, 75
- by MHRT, 91-94
- by relative, 63
- conditional, 96
Doctors
- approved, 68
- negotiating with, 54-55
- power to hold in-patient, 74
- power to bar discharge, 63
Drug abuse, 6
Drugs (medication), 103 et seq

ECT, 25, 89
Elements of social work, 47-57
Emergency admission, 71
Endogenous depression, 22-25

Functions of ASW, 44-47

Guardianship, 75-78
- by Courts, 83, 86

Hallucinations
- auditory, 31
- visual, 18
Hebephrenic schizophrenia, 32
Hospital Order, 83
- interim, 82

111

Holding power
- doctors, 74
- nurses, 74
Hypomania, 26

Illness, mental, 6
Impairment, mental, 6, 38-40
Inadequate psychopath, 43
Informal admission, 65-67
Interim Hospital Order, 82
Interpreters, 51
Interview, 50-53
Involutional Melancholia, 23

Laing, R D, 8
Local authorities, functions of, 98-99

Magistrates' Court, 81
- warrant, 79
Managers
- appeal to, 75
- discharge by, 75
Mania, 26-27
Manic depression, 22
Medical Recommendations, 68-70
Medication, 103-108
Mental Handicap, 6, 38-40
Mental Health Act Commission, 100
Mental Health Review Tribunal, 91-97
Mental Impairment, 7, 38-40
Multi-infarct brain failure, 21

National Assistance Act 1948, 57, 80
Nearest relative, 60-64
- and MHRT, 91-92
- consultation, 44, 53, 57, 63, 72
- discharge by, 63
- displacement of, 62
Neuroses, 13-19
Nurse's holding power, 74

Obligations to relatives, 53-54
Obsessive-compulsive neurosis, 14
Organic psychoses, 18-21

Paranoid schizophrenia, 32

Paraphrenia, 33
Phobias, 12-13
Place of Safety, 79-80
Police and Criminal Evidence Act, 80
Police, powers of, 80
Probation Orders, 84
Psychopathic disorder, 41-43
Psychoses, 17-27

Reactive depression, 14-16
Recommendations, Medical, 68-70
Referrals, 49-50
Relative, nearest, 60-64
- and MHRT, 91-92
- discharge by, 63
- displacement of, 62
Remand
- for reports, 81
- for treatment, 82
Removal of patient, 56-57
Renewal of detention, 73
Restriction Direction, 85
Restriction Order, 84

Schizophrenia, 28-34
- social work with, 35-37
Second Opinion Appointed Doctor, 89
Section 2, 70
Section 3, 72
Section 4, 71
Section 5, 74
Section 7, 75
Section 135, 78-80
Section 136, 80
Senile dementia, 19-20
Severe mental impairment, 6
Step-by-Step through the Act, 109
Supervision and Treatment Order, 85
Szasz, T S, 9

Toxic confusional state, 18
Transfer Direction, 85
Treatment, consent to, 87-90, 102
Tribunals (MHRT), 91-97

Warrant (Section 135), 78-80